Cloning & Stem Cells

Series Editor: Cara Acred

Volume 282

Independence Educational Publishers

First published by Independence Educational Publishers

The Studio, High Green

Great Shelford

Cambridge CB22 5EG

England

© Independence 2015

British Library Cataloguing in Publication Data

Cloning & stem cells. -- (Issues ; 282)

1. Cloning. 2. Cloning--Moral and ethical aspects. 3. Stem
cells--Transplantation. 4. Stem cells--Transplantation--
Moral and ethical aspects.

I. Series II. Acred, Cara editor.

174.2'8-dc23

ISBN-13: 9781861687104

Printed in Great Britain
Zenith Print Group

Contents

Introduction

Cloning & Stem Cells is Volume 282 in the **ISSUES** series. The aim of the series is to offer current, diverse information about important issues in our world, from a UK perspective.

ABOUT CLONING & STEM CELLS

Cloning and stem cell technology continue to advance year-on-year. This book explores the implications of human and animal cloning, and looks at how stem cell transplants are helping medicine to develop. Alongside these topics, *Cloning & Stem Cells* considers the ethical component of the cloning debate and asks what the future may hold.

OUR SOURCES

Titles in the **ISSUES** series are designed to function as educational resource books, providing a balanced overview of a specific subject.

The information in our books is comprised of facts, articles and opinions from many different sources, including:

⇨ Newspaper reports and opinion pieces

⇨ Website factsheets

⇨ Magazine and journal articles

⇨ Statistics and surveys

⇨ Government reports

⇨ Literature from special interest groups

A NOTE ON CRITICAL EVALUATION

Because the information reprinted here is from a number of different sources, readers should bear in mind the origin of the text and whether the source is likely to have a particular bias when presenting information (or when conducting their research). It is hoped that, as you read about the many aspects of the issues explored in this book, you will critically evaluate the information presented.

It is important that you decide whether you are being presented with facts or opinions. Does the writer give a biased or unbiased report? If an opinion is being expressed, do you agree with the writer? Is there potential bias to the 'facts' or statistics behind an article?

ASSIGNMENTS

In the back of this book, you will find a selection of assignments designed to help you engage with the articles you have been reading and to explore your own opinions. Some tasks will take longer than others and there is a mixture of design, writing and research-based activities that you can complete alone or in a group.

FURTHER RESEARCH

At the end of each article we have listed its source and a website that you can visit if you would like to conduct your own research. Please remember to critically evaluate any sources that you consult and consider whether the information you are viewing is accurate and unbiased.

Useful weblinks

www.alphagalileo.org

www.bionews.org.uk

www.cancerresearchuk.org

www.ciwf.org.uk

www.clonesafety.org

www.corethics.org

www.eurostemcell.org

www.filmhub.broadway.org.uk

www.occupycorporatism.com

www.politics.co.uk

www.slohorsenews.net

www.tutorhunt.com

Cloning

What is cloning?

Cloning is one of the most controversial areas of scientific research of recent times. The term 'cloning' means the asexual reproduction of identical copies of an original, and it is human cloning (and to a lesser extent animal cloning) for reproductive purposes that causes considerable public disquiet.

However, reproductive cloning is one of just three distinctive types of processes and technology covered by the term 'cloning'. The others are recombinant DNA technology or DNA cloning, and therapeutic cloning.

While there are numerous problems of technique, side-effects and technology still to overcome, the key issue in the cloning debate is generally still regarded as the ethical question – is cloning morally acceptable?

Background

The types of cloning differ widely from one another, both in their techniques and aims.

'Recombinant DNA technology', 'DNA cloning', 'molecular cloning' or 'gene cloning' all describe the process of transferring a DNA fragment from one organism to a self-replicating genetic element (a cloning vector) such as a bacterial plasmid, enabling the fragment to be propagated in an alien host.

DNA cloning is an important technique in researching gene therapy, genetic engineering of organisms, and sequencing genomes.

Reproductive cloning and therapeutic cloning both rely on the process of 'somatic cell nuclear transfer'. In this process, the nucleus of a donor adult cell is transferred to an egg whose nucleus, and thus its genetic material, has been removed. The egg is then treated with electricity in order to stimulate division.

For reproductive cloning – which creates animals with an identical genetic make-up to an already existing animal – the embryo must then be transferred to a host body, in which to grow.

For therapeutic or embryo cloning, the objective is not to create adult animals, but to extract stem cells for research from the cloned embryos created. Embryonic stem cells are extracted from the five-day-old embryo, or blastocyte, which is then destroyed.

There are hopes in the medical community that stem cell research and therapeutic cloning will facilitate organ cloning and enable the replacement of damaged cells with healthy ones for sufferers of degenerative diseases.

Although the first cloned animal – a tadpole – was created in 1952, the most publicly significant event in the history of cloning was the creation of Dolly the sheep in 1996 at the Roslin Institute, near Edinburgh. Since Dolly, a number of other cloned animals have been bred, including sheep, goats,

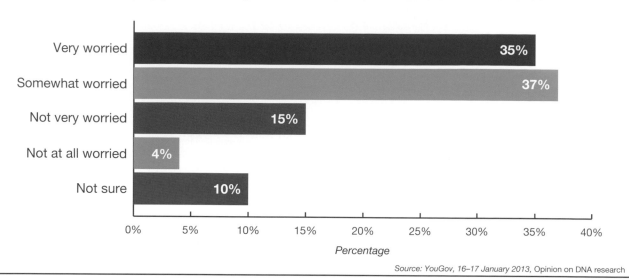

Worried about genetic research?

How worried are you, if at all, that scientific research into human or animal DNA might lead to scientists 'playing god' with things that should remain outside the realm of science?

- Very worried: 35%
- Somewhat worried: 37%
- Not very worried: 15%
- Not at all worried: 4%
- Not sure: 10%

Percentage

Source: YouGov, 16–17 January 2013, Opinion on DNA research

cows, mice, pigs, cats, rabbits, and a gaur (an endangered species of Asian bison).

However, almost as significant as Dolly's development to adulthood were the circumstances of her death. Dolly died in February 2003, with lung cancer and crippling arthritis, aged six – half the life expectancy for a sheep of her breed.

In November 2001, scientists from Advanced Cell Technologies, a biotechnology company in Massachusetts, announced that they had cloned the first human embryos for the purpose of advancing therapeutic research.

Since then, a number of more or less reputable organisations and scientists claim to have successfully brought a cloned human embryo to term – but none have been able or willing to confirm this.

Controversies

Controversies about cloning can be broken down into ethical and scientific problems, although there is a degree of overlap.

On the ethical side, it is frequently asked whether it is appropriate to 'play God' by interfering with genetics. Beyond this, critics cite the

suffering of laboratory animals, the destruction of unwanted embryos and concerns about the future uses of this new technology.

On the scientific front, the principal objection to reproductive cloning is the enormous inefficiency of the process, which may require hundreds of attempts to create a viable animal. In addition to low success rates, clones seem to suffer numerous health problems for reasons that are yet unknown.

Cloned animals tend to have compromised immune function and higher rates of infection, tumour growth, and other disorders. Studies of cloned mice and cattle show considerably reduced life expectancy. In this context, many scientists feel that, although human cloning may be possible, it would be wrong.

In December 2006 a government white paper proposed a ban on the creation of part-animal, part-human embryos after a consultation revealed widespread unease with the practice.

MPs argued against the ban, however. The Commons' science committee said in May 2007 it should be allowed under licence because existing research practices provide 'essential tools in understanding diseases'.

In 2005 Professor Ian Wilmut, the creator of Dolly the Sheep, was granted a licence to clone human embryos for medical research – a decision which attracted considerable criticism. Professor Wilmut stressed that he and his team had no intention of trying to produce cloned humans, but intended only to use the embryos for research into the distressing degenerative condition Motor Neuron Disease.

However, in 2007 Professor Wilmut announced that he had decided to change to an alternative method of research pioneered in Japan, known as direct reprogramming or 'de-differentiation', which could create human embryonic cells without using human eggs or cloning human embryos. Professor Wilmut said he believed this more ethically acceptable method had greater potential and he would therefore not be pursuing nuclear transfer.

Another area of controversy is the use of cloned animals and their descendants in food products, with concerns raised about food safety, animal welfare and ethical issues.

In 2008, the European Parliament voted for a ban on the sale of meat and milk from clones and their offspring and in October 2010 the European Commission recommended a five-year ban on animal cloning for food production in the EU, and on the use of cloned farm animals and the marketing of food from clones.

However, attempts to translate this into legislation have proved difficult. In March 2011, Commissioner John Dalli expressed his disappointment that despite the best efforts of the Commission to act as mediator between the Parliament and the Council, agreement still had not been reached on revising the regulation.

The UK Government said it believed a ban would be 'disproportionate in terms of food safety and animal welfare' and that the welfare of all farmed animals, including clones and their descendants, was already protected by current welfare legislation.

Meat and milk from cloned animals are classed as 'novel foods' under the EU Novel Foods Regulation 1997. The regulation requires that such products be assessed for safety before they can be legally marketed anywhere in the EU.

In May 2011, the Food Standards Agency attracted controversy by changing its advice on the Novel Foods Regulation in relation to the descendants of cloned cattle and pigs. The FSA Board said there were no food safety grounds for regulating food such as meat and milk from cloned descendants.

Equally controversial was the Board's decision that mandatory labelling of meat and milk derived from descendants of cloned animals was 'unnecessary and disproportionate', as was Defra's statement that such labelling would be 'unenforceable and impracticable'.

Statistics

⇨ Dolly, the first mammal to be cloned from adult DNA, was created in 1996 and died, having been put down by lethal injection, on 14 February 2003.

⇨ Prior to her death, Dolly had been suffering from lung cancer and crippling arthritis.

⇨ Most Finn Dorset sheep live to be 11 to 12 years of age.

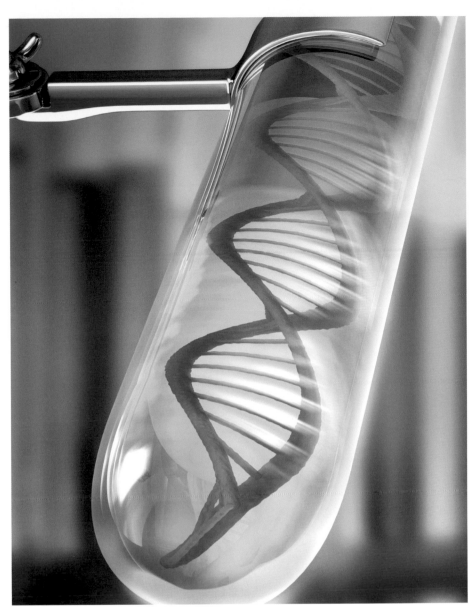

⇨ Dolly was a mother to six lambs, bred the old-fashioned way.

Source: Human Genome Project Information website.

Quotes

'A person who places in a woman a human embryo which has been created otherwise than by fertilisation is guilty of an offence.'

Human Reproductive Cloning Act

'There are perfectly ethical ways of obtaining stem cells to cure disease, which do not involve embryo destruction, so no matter what moral value one places on the human embryo, we do not need to use it.'

Josephine Quintaville – Comment on Reproductive Ethics

'Cloning for purely commercial purposes is not currently covered by any regulation but the welfare of all farmed animals is regulated in the UK through a combination of EU and national legislation. Donor animals, surrogate mothers and clones themselves would be subject to the same welfare requirements as those that apply to all farmed animals.'

Defra – 2011

⇨ The above information is reprinted with kind permission from Politics.co.uk. Please visit www.politics.co.uk for further information.

© Politics.co.uk 2015

A timeline of the evolution of animal breeding

Want to know more about the history of animal cloning? Here is a timeline of milestones in the science and production of cloned livestock.

1322
Arab chieftains first use artificial insemination to produce superior horses.

1663
Hooke discovers the existence of the cell.

1677
Leeuwenhoek sees spermatozoa through a microscope.

1780
Spallanzani discovers that a dog could be impregnated with the cellular portion of semen and that spermatozoa could be inactivated by cooling and then reactivated later.

1863
Mendel, in his study of peas, discovers that traits are transmitted from parents to progeny by discrete, independent units, later called genes. His observations lay the groundwork for the field of genetics.

1869
Miescher discovers DNA in the sperm of trout.

1891
Walter Heap performs the first successful Embryo Transfer in England with rabbits.

1894
Hans Dreisch creates the first cloned animals by blastomere transfer. He isolates blastomeres from 2- and 4-cell sea urchin embryos and observes their development into small larvae.

1900
The Russian throne hires Ivanoff to develop Artificial Insemination for horses.

1902
Hans Spemman uses a hair from his infant son as a knife to separate a 2-celled embryo from a salamander, which grows externally, and later a 16-celled embryo, all of which develop into adult salamanders.

1903
U.S. Department of Agriculture employee Herbert Webber coins the word 'clon' (which evolves into 'clone') to refer to 'any group of cells or organisms produced asexually from a single sexually produced ancestor'.

1928
Spemann performs the first nuclear transfer procedure using salamander embryos.

1937
First commercial use of Artificial Insemination by E.J. Perry.

1938
Spemann proposes a 'fantastical experiment' to clone adult somatic cells by nuclear transfer, but cannot perform the experiment because he lacks the necessary technology.

1944
DNA is proven to carry genetic information by Avery.

1950
Artificial insemination of livestock using frozen semen (a long-time dream of farmers) is successfully accomplished.

1952
Briggs and King use nuclear transfer of adult donor cells to clone frogs.

1953
Nature publishes James Watson's and Francis Crick's manuscript describing the double helical structure of DNA, which marks the beginning of the modern era of genetics.

1953
First report of cloning by nuclear transfer seen in newts.

1959
M.C. Chang reports the first unequivocal case of a live birth following egg fertilisation in the lab, true *in vitro* fertilisation, and subsequent embryo transfer, to the uterus.

1963
In China, embryologist Tong Dizhou clones a fish.

1972
First report of successful freezing of embryos. Mice embryos survive being frozen to minus 196 and 269 degrees Celsius.

1977
Somatic cell nuclear transfer used to produce cloned frogs.

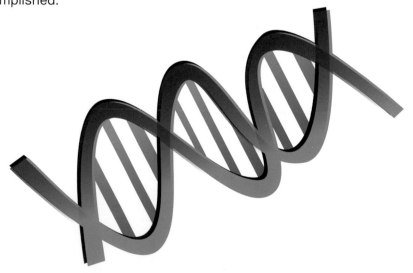

1979
A sheep is cloned by embryo splitting.

1983
First mammal produced by embryonic nuclear transfer.

1984
Creation of sheep 'identical twins' by embryo splitting.

1986
First report of embryonic cell nuclear transfer in an agricultural species (sheep).

1987
Embryonic cell nuclear transfer in cattle.

1989
Sheep and cow embryos cloned, thus pointing out that existing reproductive technology would open the way for large scale cloning in livestock.

1993
Repeated cycles (multiple generations) of nuclear transfer procedures used to produce a large number of identical animals.

1996
First report of a mammal cloned from an embryo-derived cell culture. All prior nuclear transfer had used cells from embryos rather than from cell lines established from embryos. This made it possible to easily clone an unlimited number of animals from a single embryo.

1996
The Roslin Institute in Scotland produces a sheep, Dolly, the first mammal cloned from a cell of an adult animal.

1997
Infigen, Inc. produces Gene, the first cloned cow, from a foetal cell.

1998
Genzyme Transgenic Corporation and Tufts University produce Mira, the first goat cloned from an embryonic cell.

University of Hawaii clones three generations of mice from nuclei of adult ovarian cumulus cells.

Noto and Kaga, the first cows cloned from adult cells, are produced by the Ishikawa Prefectural Livestock Research Center.

2000
The University of Teramo in Italy clones the first mouflon, a rare type of sheep, from an adult cell.

Researchers at PPL Therapeutics produce Millie, Christa, Alexis, Carrel, and Dotcom, the first pigs cloned from adult cells.

2001
Noah, a gaur and the first of an endangered species to be cloned, is produced by Advanced Cell Technologies.

CC, the first female cat cloned and the first clone of a domestic animal, is produced by Genetic Savings & Clone.

University of Georgia and Prolinia clone a cow from a kidney cell drawn from a carcass.

2002
National Academies of Science releases Animal Biotechnology: Science Based Concerns (http://www.nap.edu/books/0309084393/html).

2003
FDA issues the draft executive summary of its Assessment of Safety of Animal Cloning. (http://www.fda.gov/bbs/topics/NEWS/2003/NEW00968.html).

Trans Ova Genetics and Advanced Cell Technologies produce the first bantengs (an endangered species) cloned from adult cells.

Ditteaux, the first African wildcat cloned from an adult cell, is produced by the Audubon Center for Research of Endangered Species.

Dewey, the first deer cloned from an adult cell, is produced by ViaGen and Texas A&M shortly before Christmas.

Idaho Gem, the first mule cloned from a mule fetus, is produced by the University of Idaho.

2004
National Academies of Science releases Safety of Genetically Engineered Foods: Approaches to Assessing Unintended Health Effects and concludes that food produced from clones and their offspring are safe for human consumption (http://www.nap.edu/books/0309092094/html).

Tabouli and Baba Ganoush are the first cats cloned using chromatin transfer technology (CT).

2005
ViaGen, Inc. clones three calves from rare Prime Yield Grade 1 and 2 beef carcasses.

Snuppy, the first clone of a dog, is produced at Seoul National University in South Korea.

Audubon Center for Research of Endangered Species naturally breeds unrelated African wildcat clones, which then gave birth to the first offspring of unrelated clones of a wild species.

2006
The U.S. Food and Drug Administration (FDA) issued three documents on the safety of animal cloning – a draft risk assessment; a proposed risk management plan; and a draft guidance for industry.

⇨ The US FDA and animal cloning: Risk and regulatory approach. October 2006

⇨ A Risk-Based Approach to Evaluate Animal Clones and Their Progeny - DRAFT. 2006-2007.

⇨ US Food and Drug Administration. 2003. Animal Cloning: A Risk Assessment.

2007
The International Embryo Transfer Society hosted a symposium, 'Assisted Reproductive Technologies and Food Safety in Farm Animals,' in Kyoto, Japan. Presenters from seven countries presented data in agreement with the FDA's Draft Risk Assessment.

⇨ The above information is reprinted with kind permission from CloneSafety.org. Please visit www.clonesafety.org for further information.

© CloneSafety.org 2015

International human embryo laws

Australia

⇨ Research Involving Human Embryos Act (2002) and Prohibition of Human Cloning Act (2002): Allow research on excess IVF embryos including for derivation of human embryonic stem cells and prevent cloning

⇨ Prohibition of Human Cloning for Reproduction and the Regulation of Human Embryo Research Amendment Bill (2006): Allows somatic cell nuclear transfer (SCNT) and prohibits reproductive cloning

⇨ Use of non-human animal eggs to make SCNT cell lines prohibited

Austria

⇨ Reproductive Medicine Act (Fortpflanzungsmedizingesetz) (2004): Research on embryos, including derivation of stem cell lines, is banned

⇨ Use of embryos created legally abroad or for non-research purposes is legal

⇨ Use of imported embryonic stem cell lines is permissible and can be used for assisted reproduction

Belgium

⇨ Allow creation of human embryos for procurement of human embryonic stem cells

Bulgaria

⇨ Bulgarian Health Act (2005): Surplus embryos can be used for research purposes, subject to informed consent from donors

⇨ Reproductive cloning prohibited

Canada

⇨ Assisted Human Production Act (AHRA) (2004): Prohibits the creation of human embryos solely for germline engineering (inheritable genetic modification), the creation of human or non-human hybrids and chimeras, all use of SCNT cloning whether for research or reproduction, and sex selection except to prevent, diagnose, or treat a sex-linked disorder or disease. Research involving human embryos permitted, using created embryos not used during IVF procedures[1]

China

⇨ Restrictions in place for human embryonic stem cell research and derivation[2]

Czech Republic

⇨ Act on Research on Human Embryonic Stem Cells and Related Activities (2006): Research may be conducted on embryonic stem cell lines imported into the country or derived from surplus IVF embryos not older than seven days with donor informed consent. It is permitted if it will advance scientific or medical knowledge, lead to the development of new treatments or cures for serious diseases, and where expected scientific benefits can't be reached by other methods

⇨ Reproductive cloning banned

Finland

⇨ Medical Research Act 1999/4888: Can derive legally from excess IVF embryos up to 14 days after fertilisation or must be destroyed. May also be frozen for up to 15 years and then must be destroyed. Creation of embryos for research banned unless specifically for finding new cures and treatments for serious diseases

⇨ Act on Medical Use of Organs and Tissues (2001): Embryos can only be used for fertility treatment or medical research

⇨ Embryo: 'Living group of cells resulting from fertilisation not implanted in a woman's body'

⇨ SCNT not forbidden

France

⇨ Law on Bioethics (2004) and Amendment (2011): Prohibit use of IVF human embryos and embryonic stem cells for research unless:

1. Research is scientifically relevant

2. Research is likely to allow major medical advances

3. Expressly established research can't be performed unless cells derived from embryos are used

4. Project respects French ethical principles for research on embryos and embryonic stem cell lines

⇨ Human cloning banned

⇨ Creation of embryos specifically for research is banned

---

1 http://www.geneticsandsociety.org/article.php?id=335

2 www.stemgen.org

⇨ Embryonic stem cells can be imported with permission by Agence de la Biomedicine

Germany

⇨ Constitution (Grundgesetz): Embryo is protected. 'Human dignity is inviolable'. 'Everyone has the right to life and inviolability of his person'

⇨ Embryo Protection Act (Embryonenschutzgesetz) (1991): Derivation of embryonic stem cell lines is a criminal offence

⇨ Stem Cell Act (2002) (amended in 2008): Lengthened cut-off point to 1 May 2007 as to when embryonic stem cell lines must have been derived

⇨ Banned human cloning

⇨ Importation of embryonic stem cell lines permitted under strict conditions and must be approved by the Central Ethics Commission for Stem Cell Research

⇨ Embryonic stem cell lines can only be used if vital in developing new scientific and medical knowledge

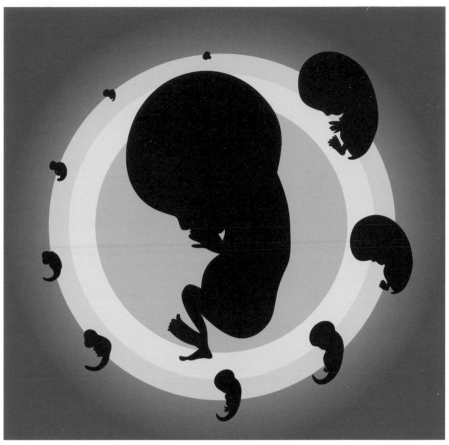

Greece

⇨ Article 1459 of Law 3089/2002: Use of surplus reproductive material for research allowed, subject to donor's consent. Embryos may be frozen for as many as five years and then must either be destroyed or used for therapeutic or research purposes. Fertilised eggs not frozen must be destroyed 14 days after fertilisation

⇨ Human reproductive cloning expressly prohibited

Hungary

⇨ Art. II of the Constitution: Human dignity shall be inviolable. Every human being shall have the right to life and human dignity; embryonic and foetal life shall be subject to protection from the moment of conception[3]

⇨ No specific legislation regarding human embryonic stem cell research

Ireland

⇨ Constitution: Protects 'the right to life of the unborn and, with due regard to the equal right to life of the mother' in cases of pregnancy terminations

⇨ M.R. v. T.R. Case (2009): An embryo created outside of the womb is not protected under the Constitution

⇨ Irish Medical Council (2009): Banned medical practitioners from creating embryos specifically for research

⇨ No regulation for stem cell research

Israel

⇨ Ban human cloning

⇨ Permit therapeutic cloning

Italy

⇨ Law 40 (2004): Embryo has rights from moment of fertilisation. No research on the embryo unless it specifically helps improving the therapeutic and medical condition of that particular embryo

⇨ Ban deriving embryonic stem cell lines

⇨ Allow use of imported embryonic stem cell lines

Japan

⇨ Ban human cloning

⇨ Permit therapeutic cloning

⇨ Permissive approach to human embryonic stem cell research derivation[4]

3   https://www.constituteproject.org/constitution/Hungary_2011

4   www.stemgen.org

Strongly approve
4%

Not sure
12%

Somewhat approve
12%

Somewhat disapprove
20%

Strongly disapprove
52%

Source: YouGov/Huffington Post survey of 1000 US adults interviewed January 16 - 17, 2014 on genetic research

⇨ Constitutional Court: The principle of the rule of law includes safeguards for the protection of human life at every stage of its development and guarantees the protection of health of the foetus and its smooth development. The unborn have a right to life from conception

⇨ No specific legislation regarding human embryonic stem cell research

Portugal

⇨ Law No. 32/2006: Research limited to frozen or surplus embryos that can bring potential therapeutic and medical benefits to humanity. Bans creation of embryos for research and makes it criminal to improperly research into embryos

⇨ Allow derivation of human embryonic stem cell lines from surplus IVF embryos

Lithuania

⇨ Law on Ethics of Biomedical Research No. VIII-1679 (2000): Use of embryos for research restricted to observation and non-interventional trials

⇨ Prohibit import and export of tissues of human embryo, embryonic stem cells, and lines

⇨ Prohibit research on human embryos

New Zealand[5]

⇨ Human Assisted Reproductive Technology Act (2004): Prohibit artificially forming a cloned or hybrid embryo for reproductive purposes. Prohibit implanting into a human being a cloned embryo; an animal gamete or embryo; a hybrid embryo; a genetically modified gamete, human, or hybrid embryo; or a gamete or embryo derived from a foetus. Prohibit implanting an animal with a human gamete or embryo, or a hybrid embryo

⇨ Illegal to commercially supply human embryos

Poland

⇨ Art. 38 of the Constitution: Guarantees protection of human life at any stage (including prenatal) during the development phase and protection of the health of the foetus and its smooth development

⇨ Art. 39 of the Constitution: No one shall be subjected to scientific experimentation, including medical experimentation, without his voluntary consent[6]

⇨ Act 7.01.1993: Right to life is protected, including in the prenatal phase

Russia

⇨ Art. 20 of the Constitution: Everyone shall have the right to life[7]

⇨ Art. 21 of the Constitution: Human dignity shall be protected by the State. Nothing may serve as a basis for its derogation. Nobody may be subjected to medical, scientific, or other experiments without voluntary consent

⇨ Ban human cloning[8]

Spain

⇨ Law 14/2007: Allows research on embryos for therapeutic and research purposes. Prohibits creation of embryos for research. Forbids reproductive human cloning

⇨ Law 35/1988: Bans research on viable embryos unless for purposes of diagnosing, treating or preventing disease in that embryo

⇨ Law 45/2003: Permits donation of embryos for research

⇨ Law 22/2006: Allows surplus embryos to be donated for reproductive purposes towards a specific research objective or to be disposed of

Sweden

⇨ Activities Involving Human Eggs for Research of Treatment Purposes Act (1991): Permits research on excess IVF embryos up to 14 days after fertilisation and their destruction afterwards

⇨ Act on Genetic Integrity (2005): Allows creation of

5   http://www.legislation.govt.nz/act/public/2004/0092/latest/whole.html

6   https://www.constituteproject.org/constitution/Poland_1997

7   https://www.constituteproject.org/constitution/Russia_2008

8   www.ruf.rice.edu

human embryos for research using SCNT therapeutic cloning after ethics committee approval

⇨ Reproductive cloning banned

Switzerland

⇨ Constitution: Human dignity enjoys protection especially from being misused by regenerative medical therapies, gene technology and other reproductive technologies

⇨ Federal Act on Research Involving Embryonic Stem Cells (2003): Surplus IVF embryos can be used for research under strict licensing conditions and are subject to consent. Surplus embryos can only be kept for research purposes and must be destroyed following their use. Allows importation of embryonic stem cell lines specifically for research purposes

⇨ Embryonic stem cells can be derived from surplus IVF embryos up to seven days old

United Kingdom

⇨ Human Fertilisation and Embryology Act (1990) and Human Fertilisation and Embryology (Research Purposes) Regulations (2001): Embryonic stem cell research must be absolutely necessary for research purposes and only done with a licence from the Human Fertilisation and Embryology Authority (HFEA), including: promoting advances in treatment of infertility; increasing knowledge about causes of congenital disease, causes of miscarriages, development of embryos, and serious disease; developing more effective techniques of contraception and methods for detecting presence of gene or chromosome abnormalities; and enabling any such knowledge to be applied in developing treatments for serious disease

⇨ Human Reproductive Cloning Act (2001): Illegal to use cell replacement to create child[9]

⇨ Amendment (2008): Allowed to add limited amounts of animal cells to human chimeras, true hybrids, and transgenic human embryos

⇨ Bans human reproductive cloning

⇨ Permits therapeutic cloning

⇨ Legally permits creation of human embryos for procurement of human embryonic stem cells

⇨ Can only research embryos up to 14 days old created through IVF

United States

⇨ Dickey-Wicker Amendment: Prohibits destruction of human embryos[10]

⇨ Human embryonic stem cell research permitted

⇨ Impossible to create new human embryonic stem cell lines from viable embryos using federal funds at the federal level

⇨ Much variance among the states, but in California, researchers may create new human embryonic stem cell lines

⇨ Private funding of embryonic stem cell research has never been prohibited or regulated[11]

European Union

⇨ Ban funding of human cloning

⇨ Refuse to fund research using somatic cell nuclear transfer to create embryos

⇨ Support funding embryonic stem cell research

⇨ The above information is reprinted with kind permission from Comment on Reproductive Ethics (CORE). Please visit www.corethics.org for further information.

© Comment on Reproductive Ethics (CORE) 2015

9 www.eurostemcell.org

10 www.nature.com

11 www.eurostemcell.org

Reproductive cloning

Adult being cloned

Skin cells are taken from the adult being cloned

Adult female

An unfertilised egg is taken from an adult female

The nucleus is removed from the egg

The skin cell is placed next to the unfertilised, nucleus-free, egg and an electric pulse causes them to fuse together

The fused cell, which contains the skin cell's nucleus, divides to form an early-stage embryo

The embryo is then implanted into a surrogate mother

The cloned animal is born!

Source: www.genome.gov

Myths about cloning

The responses to the questions provided in this document represent the FDA's view in light of the conclusions and recommendations outlined in the Animal Cloning Risk Assessment, Risk Management Plan and Guidance for Industry #179.

Myth: Cloning is a new technology

Actually, cloning isn't new at all. In fact, we eat fruit from plant clones all the time, in the form of bananas and grafted fruits. We've been cloning plants for decades, except that we refer to it as 'vegetative propagation'. It takes about 30 years to breed a banana from seed, so, to speed the process of getting fruit to market, most bananas, potatoes, apples, grapes, pears and peaches are from clones.

Some animals can reproduce themselves by vegetative propagation, including starfish and other relatively simple sea creatures. Amphibians such as frogs first underwent cloning in the 1950s. Identical twin mammals can be thought of as naturally occurring clones, but producing clones of mammals in the laboratory is relatively new. Using cells from animal embryos to make clones has been has been around since the early 1990s, but the first animal cloned from a cell from an adult animal was Dolly the sheep, who was born in 1996.

Myth: Clones are a specific animal's DNA grafted onto another body

Absolutely not. Despite science fiction books and movies, clones are born just like any other animal. The only difference is that clones don't require a sperm and egg to come together to make an embryo. Clone embryos are made by using a whole cell or cell nucleus from a donor animal and fusing it to an egg cell that's had its nucleus removed. That embryo is implanted into the uterus of a surrogate dam (a livestock term that breeders use to refer to the female parent of an animal) to grow just as if it came from embryo transfer or *in vitro* fertilisation.

Myth: Offspring of clones are clones, and each generation gets weaker and weaker and has more and more problems

No, not at all. A clone produces offspring by sexual reproduction just like any other animal. A farmer or breeder can use natural mating or any other assisted reproductive technology, such as artificial insemination or *in vitro* fertilisation to breed clones, just as they do for other farm animals. The offspring are not clones, and are the same as any other sexually-reproduced animals.

Myth: Clones are always identical in looks

Not necessarily. In fact, many clones have slight variations in coat colour and markings.

Let's think about the identical twin calves again. They have the same genes, but look a little different. That's because of the way those genes are expressed – that is, how the information in that gene is seen in the actual animal. For example, if they're Holstein cows, the pattern of their spots, or the shape of their ears may be different. Human identical twins also have the same genes, but because those genes are expressed differently in each person, they have different freckle and fingerprint patterns.

Myth: Clones have exactly the same temperament and personality as the animals from which they were cloned

Temperament is only partly determined by genetics; a lot has to do with the way an animal has been raised. It's the old 'nature versus nurture' argument.

Say you want to clone your horse because of his gentle and sweet temperament. Although your horse's clone may be easy-going, he would have to have exactly the same life experiences as your original horse in order to have the same temperament.

Your original horse isn't afraid of loud noises because his experiences have taught him that they won't hurt him. But if your clone has a bad experience with loud noises (for instance, a tree branch falls on him in a loud thunderstorm and hurts him), he may associate loud noises with pain and be afraid of them.

Myth: When clones are born, they're the same age as their donors, and don't live long

Clones are born the same way as other new-born animals: as babies. No one really knows what causes aging in mammals, but most scientists think it has to do with a part of the chromosome called a telomere that functions as a kind of clock in the cell. Telomeres tend to be long at birth, and shorten as the animal ages.

A study on Dolly (the famous sheep clone) showed that her telomeres were the shorter length of her (older) donor, even though Dolly was much younger. Studies of other clones have shown that telomeres in clones are shorter in some tissues in the body, and are age-appropriate in other tissues. Still other studies of clones show that telomeres are age-appropriate in all of the tissues. Despite the length of telomeres reported in different studies, most clones appear to be aging normally. In fact, the first cattle clones ever produced are alive, healthy, and are ten years old as of January 2008.

Myth: Cloning results in severely damaged animals that suffer, and continue to have health problems all their lives

The vast majority of swine and goat clones are born healthy, grow normally, and are no more susceptible to health problems than their non-clone counterparts. During the early days of what is known as assisted reproductive technologies in livestock, veterinarians noticed that some calf and lamb foetuses grew too large during pregnancy, and had serious birth defects. This set of abnormalities is referred to as 'large offspring syndrome'. or LOS. These same abnormalities have also been seen in calf and lamb clones, and have received a lot of attention because they occur at what appear to be higher rates than observed with other assisted reproductive technologies. The syndrome seems to be related to processes that take place outside the body (during the *in vitro* phase. As producers understand more about the cloning process, the rate at which LOS is observed in calf and lamb clones has been decreasing. The same kind of decrease in LOS rates was observed as people who used technologies such as *in vitro* fertilisation in cattle learned more about the process. LOS hasn't been seen in swine or goat clones.

Most clones that are normal at birth become as strong and healthy as any other young animals. Calf and lamb clones with abnormalities at birth may continue to have health problems for the first few months of life. But after the age of six months, they're completely indistinguishable in appearance and blood measurements from conventionally bred animals of the same age.

Myth: Cow clones make human pharmaceuticals in their milk

Lots of people get this confused. The clones we're talking about here are 'just clones'. They don't have any new genes added to them, and they don't make pharmaceuticals (or any other non-milk substances) in their milk. They just do the same thing as their conventionally bred counterparts. Cows that make pharmaceuticals in their milk are genetically engineered – that is, they have new genes added to them. Some of these genetically engineered animals can be reproduced by cloning, which is why some people get confused about this concept.

Myth: When a chicken clone lays eggs, the chicks that hatch are clones

Neither chickens nor any other kind of bird have been cloned yet. So far, mice, rats, rabbits, cattle (and the closely related but endangered gaurs and bantengs), swine, sheep, goats, deer, horses, mules, cats, and dogs are the mammals that have been cloned.

Myth: Meat from clones is already in the food supply

FDA asked clone producers and breeders to voluntarily keep milk and meat from clones out of the food and feed supplies until we finish assessing their safety. To the best of our knowledge, they have done so. After years of detailed study and analysis, FDA has concluded that meat and milk from clones of cattle, swine, and goats, and the offspring of clones from any species traditionally consumed as food, are as safe to eat as food from conventionally bred animals. We don't expect food from clones to enter the food supply in any great amounts any time soon, as these animals will be used for breeding.

The U.S. Department of Agriculture (USDA) believes that it is unlikely that products from these animals would enter the meat supply for several years. Meat and milk products from the progeny of animal clones are several years off. USDA will convene stakeholders to discuss efforts to provide a smooth and orderly market transition, as industry determines next steps with respect to the existing voluntary moratorium.

Myth: Cloning can cure diseases in livestock

Cloning can't directly cure diseases in livestock, but the cloning process may be one way to make a healthy copy of a valuable animal that has contracted a disease, been injured, or died. In addition, cloning may also be a way to duplicate a disease-resistant animal, and over generations create a disease-resistant herd.

Myth: Scientists can bring back extinct species by cloning them

Although it's theoretically possible, at this time it's not very likely to happen. There are multiple technical barriers to doing this. First, because of the relatively low success rate of cloning, you'd need hundreds to thousands of cells from the extinct animal. Further, those cells would have to have DNA that hadn't degraded since the animals were last alive. Then you'd have to find a very, very closely related species to provide the egg cell whose nucleus would be removed. After that, you'd have to implant any dividing embryos into the 'normal' development environment. (You might be able to use an elephant to act as a surrogate dam for a woolly mammoth, but there is no modern animal comparable to a dinosaur.) Then, you'd have to hope that the surrogate dam didn't reject the embryo as 'too foreign'. So although it's possible, we wouldn't expect that you'd see this at this time or in the near future.

Well, okay, but how about cloning endangered species?

That's not only possible, but it's been done in some limited cases. Scientists have cloned sheep from very small populations, members of rare cattle breeds, and the gaur and banteng, two species closely related to domesticated cattle species.

7 March 2014

⇨ The above information is reprinted with kind permission from the U.S. Food and Drug Administration. Please visit www.fda.gov for further information.

Clones and eugenics in cinema

By John Marks

What we see?

Cloning and the genetic manipulation of humans – eugenics – have become established narrative tropes in cinema. The main recurring themes are filiation, human 'uniqueness' and difference, instrumentality, and totalitarian or rigidly class-based societies.

Films frequently deal with a combination of these themes. So, for example, *Gattaca* explores family relationships and the qualities that comprise our 'humanity' in the context of a future dystopia in which genetic engineering produces new class divisions. The film delivers the partially reassuring message that, by force of will, a particular individual who is defined as flawed within this society can outperform a sibling who has pre-programmed advantages.

A number of films dealing with these issues demonstrate interesting aesthetic traits. Gattaca portrays a smooth, sleek futurescape in order both to convey the controlling nature of a eugenic dystopia and also to stand in contrast to the messy material and psychological reality of human individuals and family relationships.

Code 46 portrays a dystopian future in which heavily-controlled mega-cities are surrounded by deserts and shanty towns. Citizens of these mega-cities speak a form of 'global' English incorporating words and phrases from a number of other languages. The prevalence of reproductive technologies such as IVF and cloning means that individuals need to be screened in order to prevent sexual relationships between partners who are genetically identical. In contrast to the stylistic sleekness of *Gattaca*, *Code 46* envisions a future society and humanity that is sprawling, hybrid and contingent. It is in this context that the shadowy totalitarian authority – the Sphinx –

attempts to exercise some form of genetic control over its citizens.

Drawing on the literary and psychoanalytic theme of the uncanny, there is a pervasive dreamlike quality and atmosphere of unease that manifests itself in films like *Never Let Me Go* and *Moon*. *The Boys from Brazil* and the recent *Wakolda* deal with the issue of Nazi eugenic experiments and display a variation on this theme of unease, evoking a vaguely gothic atmosphere around Josef Mengele in post-war South America. *Wakolda*'s use of the rather hackneyed imagery of identical clockwork dolls to symbolise Mengele's psychopathic drive for human uniformity evokes a gothic sense of the uncanny.

In general terms, films dealing specifically with clones or quasi-clone characters demonstrate an interesting development over time. It is possible to identify a distinct evolution running from the robotic individuals in *The Stepford Wives* to the fully human group of friends in *Never Let Me Go*. In part, this

reflects a shift away from pervasive anxieties around conformity and totalitarian regimes in the post-war era.

Ethics?

Cinema seems to be taking clones more seriously, speculating on how human they might be treated and what consequences cloning would have for human relationships. In short, cinematic clones have become more 'human', and are now increasingly shown as being subject to prejudice or marginalisation as a social group that evokes unwarranted revulsion.

Of course, the development of cinematic representations has clearly been influenced by the fact that the science of cloning has moved from the realm of speculation to reality with the birth of Dolly the sheep – the world's first successfully cloned mammal – in 1996. Techniques such as cloning, stem cell therapies and pre-implantation genetic diagnosis have become scientific realities and have been widely discussed in the media and at a governmental level.

One way in which cinematic representations of biotechnology and the human have responded to this changing scientific landscape is by speculating on the possible emergence of stark new class differences between those who can afford to avail themselves of these new opportunities to enhance and prolong their own lives, together with those of their children, and those who service these new consumer demands. The utopian blockbuster *The Island* depicts a future in which human clones are created – as in *Never Let Me Go* – to provide harvestable organs for a rich clientele. These wealthy customers are told that their organ donor clones are non-sentient organic frames – 'agnates' – whereas the clones are in fact fully human. Although very different in tone and approach, both *The Island* and *Never Let Me Go* are examples of an interesting emergent dystopian theme in

contemporary science fiction. As well as dramatising bioethical issues, these filmic dystopias clearly express contemporary anxieties around what is widely perceived to be a growing global divide between rich and poor.

A good deal of bioethical discourse around cloning and biotechnology has focused on the morality of creating an individual for instrumental reasons. As well as having what we might call biopolitical consequences, this theme raises important questions about issues of parenthood and biological filiation in general. *Womb* (released as *Clone* in the UK) explores the possibility of a mother giving birth to a clone of her dead husband in a near future in which human cloning is a viable technology.

Speculations

Unsurprisingly, human reproductive cloning is illegal in many countries around the world. However, in recent times claims have been made – notably by the Raelian

cult Clonaid in 2002 – that human cloning has been successfully carried out: these claims have never been verified and seem unlikely to be true.

Generalised, although not universal, moral aversion to the idea of human cloning, as well as the significant technical problems in perfecting these techniques, mean that the prospect of widespread reproductive cloning remains a very distant possibility. However, cloning and biotechnology in cinema is more than just a dramatic device. We may not be on the point of cloning humans, but developments, in areas like stem cell research and genetic testing, point towards a future in which life can be manipulated by technological intervention.

More to think about/ Further reading

Mark Fisher, 'Precarious Dystopias: *The Hunger Games*, *In Time*, *Never Let Me Go*', Film Quarterly, vol. 65, no. 4 (Summer 2012)

Brian Michael Goss, 'Taking Cover from Progress: Michael Winterbottom's Code 46', *Journal of Communication Inquiry*, vol. 31, no. 1 (2007)

John Harris, *On Cloning* (2004)

David A. Kirby, 'Extrapolating race in *GATTACA*: Genetic passing, Identity, and the Science of Race', *Literature and Medicine*, vol. 23, no 1 (Spring 2004)

Eric Seedhouse, *Beyond Human: Engineering our Future Evolution* (2014)

⇨ The above information is reprinted with kind permission from Film Hub Central East. Please visit www.filmhub. broadway.org.uk for further information.

Books and films with the theme of cloning

Films
⇨ *Clone* [original title: *Womb*] (2010) (15)
⇨ *Code 46* (2003) (15)
⇨ *Gattaca* (1997) (15)
⇨ *Jurassic Park* (1993) (PG)
⇨ *Never Let Me Go* (2010) (12A)
↳ *Star Wars: Episode II – Attack of the Clones* (2002) (PG)
⇨ *The 6th Day* (2000) (15)
⇨ *The Boys from Brazil* (1982) (X)
⇨ *The Fifth Element* (1997) (PG)
⇨ *The Island* (2005) (12A)

Books
⇨ *The Boys from Brazil* by Ira Levin (1976)
⇨ *Never Let Me Go* by Kazuo Ishiguro (2005)
⇨ *Jurassic Park* by Michael Crichton (1990)

Stem cell transplants

What stem cell transplants are

Stem cell transplant is a treatment to try to cure some types of leukaemia, lymphoma and other conditions affecting the bone marrow, such as myeloma. You have very high doses of chemotherapy, sometimes with whole body radiotherapy. This has a good chance of killing the cancer cells but also kills the stem cells in the bone marrow.

Stem cells are very early blood cells in the bone marrow that develop into red blood cells, white blood cells and platelets. We need stem cells in order to survive. So after the high dose treatment you have stem cells into a vein through a drip to replace those that the cancer treatment has killed.

Stem cell transplant means that you can have higher doses of treatment. So there may be more chance of curing the cancer than with standard chemotherapy.

Growth factors

You have injections of growth factors before, and sometimes after, the stem cell transplant. Growth factors are natural proteins that make the bone marrow produce blood cells. You have them as small injections under the skin.

You have daily injections of growth factor for between five and ten days. Sometimes you may have low doses of a chemotherapy drug alongside the growth factor injections. The chemotherapy and growth factor injections help your bone marrow to make lots of stem cells. These stem cells then spill out of the bone marrow into the bloodstream. You have blood tests every day to see if there are enough stem cells in your bloodstream. When there are enough stem cells, your stem cells are collected (harvested).

Growth factor injections can cause some side effects. Some people have itching around the injection site. Some people get a high temperature (fever). You may have some pain in your bones after you have had a few injections. This is because there are a lot of blood cells being made inside the bones.

Collecting the stem cells

Collecting the stem cells takes three or four hours. You will be asked to lie down on a couch. Your nurse puts a drip into each of your arms and attaches it to a machine.

Your blood passes out of one drip, through the machine and back into your body through the other drip. The machine filters the stem cells out of your blood. The stem cells are collected and frozen until you are ready to have them back.

Stages of the transplant process

Having a bone marrow transplant is a complicated five-stage process.

The five stages are:

1. **Physical examination** – to assess your general level of health.

2. **Harvesting** – the process of obtaining the stem cells to be used in the transplant. The method most commonly used in adults involves removing blood from the body, separating stem cells from the other cells in the blood and then returning the blood to the body.

3. **Conditioning** – preparing your body for the transplant.

4. **Transplanting the stem cells**

5. **Recovery period** – during which you'll be monitored for any complications or side effects.

Source: NHS Choices, 2014

It is common for patients to feel very tired after donating stem cells. You may get tingling around your mouth or muscle cramps if your calcium level gets low during the collection. If this happens doctors or nurses will give you calcium, usually through a drip.

About donor stem cells

Some people have stem cells from another person. Stem cells from another person are called donor stem cells. If you have donated stem cells they need to closely match your own. A brother or sister is most likely to be a close match. Sometimes, if you don't have a brother or sister (a sibling donor) who is a match, you can have stem cells from a donor who is not related to you but whose stem cells are similar to yours.

The donor stem cells are collected from the donor as described above.

Cord blood stem cells

Some people may have a stem cell transplant using stem cells from umbilical cord blood. There are cord blood banks which store blood taken from the umbilical cord. After the baby is born and the umbilical cord has been cut, a doctor takes blood from the umbilical cord and placenta. The blood bank may then give the donated stem cells to a person whose blood cells closely match the donated cells.

There is information about donating cord blood on the NHS cord blood bank website (www.nhsbt.nhs.uk/cordblood/) and the Anthony Nolan website (www.anthonynolan.org).

Mini transplants

Stem cells can be used in mini transplants. In a mini transplant, you have lower doses of chemotherapy than in a traditional stem cell transplant. So this treatment can be given to people who are too old or not well enough for a traditional transplant. Research is going on to see how we can best use mini transplants in leukaemia and lymphoma treatment.

More about stem cell transplants

If you would like more information about anything to do with stem cell

transplants, you can phone the Cancer Research UK nurses. The number is freephone 0808 800 4040 and the lines are open from 9am to 5pm, Monday to Friday. You can also send the nurses a question (https://www.cancerresearchuk.org/about-cancer/utilities/contact-us). They will be happy to help.

The Anthony Nolan charity has helpful information. They have a register to match people willing to donate their bone marrow or blood stem cells to people who need transplants. They also provide information, support and an on-line forum for patients and families going through a transplant. You can find out about them on their website at www.anthonynolan.org.

16 March 2015

⇨ The above information is reprinted with kind permission from Cancer Research UK patient information. Please visit www.cancerresearchuk.org/about-cancer/cancers-in-general/treatment/transplant/stem-cell-transplants for further information.

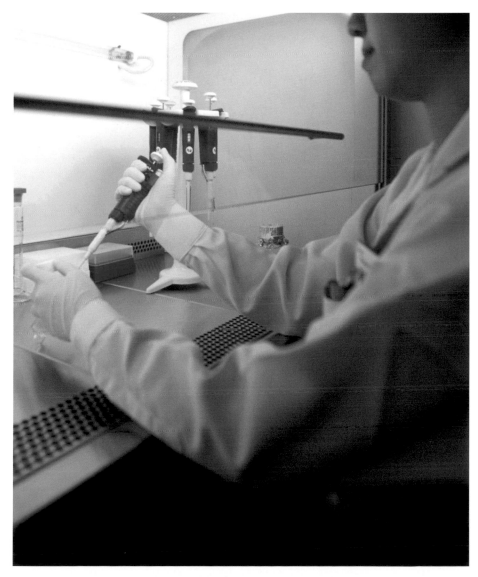

'Miracle' stem cell therapy reverses multiple sclerosis

The treatment is the first to reverse the symptoms of MS, which has no cure, and affects around 100,000 people in Britain.

By Sarah Knapton, Science Editor

A pioneering new stem cell treatment is allowing multiple sclerosis sufferers to walk, run and even dance again, in results branded 'miraculous' by doctors.

Patients who have been wheelchair-bound for ten years have regained the use of their legs in the ground-breaking therapy, while others who were blind can now see again.

The treatment is the first to reverse the symptoms of MS, which has no cure, and affects around 100,000 people in Britain.

The two dozen patients who are taking part in the trials at the Royal Hallamshire Hospital in Sheffield and Kings College Hospital, London, have effectively had their immune systems 'rebooted'.

Although it is unclear what causes MS, some doctors believe that it is the immune system itself which attacks the brain and spinal cord, leading to inflammation and pain, disability and in severe cases, death.

In the new treatment, specialists use a high dose of chemotherapy to knock out the immune system before rebuilding it with stem cells taken from the patient's own blood.

Stem cells are so effective because they can become any cell in the body based on their environment.

'Since we started treating patients three years ago, some of the results we have seen have been miraculous,' Professor Basil Sharrack, a consultant neurologist at Sheffield Teaching Hospitals NHS Foundation Trust, told *The Sunday Times*.

'This is not a word I would use lightly, but we have seen profound neurological improvements.'

During the treatment, the patient's stem cells are harvested and stored. Then doctors use aggressive drugs which are usually given to cancer patients to completely destroy the immune system.

The harvested stem cells are then infused back into the body where they start to grow new red and white blood cells within just two weeks.

Within a month the immune system is back up and running fully and that is when patients begin to notice that they are recovering.

Holly Drewry, 25, of Sheffield, was wheelchair bound after the birth of her daughter Isla, now two.

But she claims the new treatment has transformed her life.

'It worked wonders,' she said. 'I remember being in the hospital... after three weeks, I called my mum and said: "I can stand". We were all crying.

'I can run a little bit, I can dance. I love dancing, it is silly but I do. I enjoy walking my daughter around the park in her pram. It is a miracle but I can do it all.'

However, specialists warn that patients need to be fit to benefit from the new treatment.

'This is not a treatment that is suitable for everybody because it is very aggressive and patients need to be quite fit to withstand the effects of the chemotherapy,' warned Professor Sharrack.

Charities welcomed the research but also urged caution.

Dr Sorrel Bickley, Research Communications Manager at the MS Society said: 'This new study reports very encouraging findings, which add to a growing body of research into stem cell transplantation in MS. However, there are limitations to how we can interpret these results because there was no control group used, which means we can't be sure the results are robust.

'Momentum in this area of research is building rapidly and we're eagerly awaiting the results of larger, randomised trials and longer term follow-up data.

'New treatments for MS are urgently needed, but as yet there are no stem cell therapies licensed for MS anywhere in the world. This means they aren't yet established as being both safe and effective. This type of stem cell therapy is very aggressive and does carry significant risks, so we would strongly urge caution in seeking this treatment outside of a properly regulated clinical trial.'

The research was published in the *Journal of the American Medical Association*.

1 March 2015

⇨ The above information is reprinted with kind permission from *The Telegraph*. Please visit www.telegraph.co.uk for further information.

Any questions? Young people imagine a stem cell future...

By Cathy Southworth

Ever thought of the potential for stem cells to be used for making leather or clothes? Maybe not the first application that comes to mind when the focus of most stem cell research is human medicine. Future casting by young people, though, gives rise to imaginative and curious questions. Such questions have provided a wealth of discussion and wonderment during two science engagement projects aimed at young people: Regenerate! In Scotland and a stem cell revolutions film tour in Australia. We have selected some of the most common questions and asked some of our scientists to ponder how they might have answered. With thanks to the scientists for their contributions and Vanessa De Mello for her illustrations (Vanessa has recently started an internship with EuroStemCell, where her artistic talents are proving most welcome!). Look out for part two, where we tackle some of the ethical questions that arose.

Can you clone a human being using stem cells?

In principle it should be possible to clone a human being either using stem cells or associated technology.

To date this has not been done and it is questionable as to whether we are yet at the stage where we understand enough about how stem cells work to do so safely. In addition to this we need to question ourselves as to whether human cloning is morally justified, and if so in what context? It may one day be possible to use stem cell technology to clone someone who has died but is this the right thing to do? Nobel Laureate Sir John Gurdon has said in interviews that he believes if human cloning can be used to alleviate suffering and improve human health then it will be widely accepted by the public. What do you think?

Answered by James Hackland

What do stem cells have to do with cancer?

The blood system is an excellent example for studying the involvement of stem cells in cancer formation. Normal blood stem cells are found in the bone marrow and produce the red and white blood cells we need throughout our life. They divide to produce more stem cells (called self-renewal) and differentiate to

generate all blood cells. In blood cancers such as leukaemias, normal stem cells are damaged and turn into cancer stem cells that self-renew uncontrollably and are no longer able to make normal blood cells. Instead, these cancer stem cells fuel the disease by generating the bulk of the tumour and are very difficult to remove using current treatments. This example of cancer stem cells in leukaemia applies to many other cancers, including bowel cancer and breast cancer. In order to develop therapies to cure cancers we need to work out how to target the cancer stem cells and kill them.

Answered by Kamil Kranc

Could we make leather from stem cells, to make shoes and bags?

You would be able to grow cow skin stem cells in a dish, but the problem is that the skin used for skin grafts, grown in a dish, doesn't get the chance to form the dry upper cornified layers that would make up the toughness of leather. If you could find a way of growing it on a slightly damp nutrient base that is exposed to air on top, similar to our actual skin, the cells

might spontaneously make these tough upper layers. So the answer is that it might be possible. But the texture would be different – there are no hairs, so it would be completely smooth; and it would be colourless. Perhaps that could turn out to be a desirable fashion material of the future, though!

Answered by Val Wilson

How do you control stem cells and make them into the cells you want?

This is a big question and has occupied the minds of many stem cell scientists all over the world for the past few years!

Mostly, people add proteins or chemicals to the liquid medium that most stem cells grow in. These are factors that people know that cells are exposed to in a living organism, and the trick is to use the right factors in the right sequence – we don't always know which factors are important to steer cells through a series of intermediate steps to a final, desired cell type. So, very often there is a series of five or six, or even more, steps where the cells are exposed to different factors to make cells like the insulin-producing cells of the pancreas, or nerve, muscle or bone cells – in some human cells these protocols can take a month or more to make a cell type of interest!

Answered by Val Wilson

Can one type of cell be artificially changed to another type of cell inside your body?

Yes, this can be done by adding powerful (dominant) genes known as transcription factors into the cells of a specific part of the body, usually with a virus. The first and best example came from a group of scientists led by Doug Melton. He turned cells found in the pancreas called exocrine cells into insulin-producing beta-cells in mice. He gave the exocrine cells 3 transcription factors (Ngn3, Pdx1 and MafA).

Answered by Tilo Kunath

How do you become a stem cell scientist? Three different countries, three similar stories:

Answered by James Hackland who went to school in England

If you want to be a stem cell scientist you need to do well in biology and chemistry at A-level so that you can go on to do a biological undergraduate degree at university such as Biochemistry or Biomedical Science. Once you have done this you can progress to a doctorate in a lab that carries out stem cell research. Although you do need to do well at school, the most important ingredient to a good scientist is enthusiasm. Science is as much a hobby as it is a job. Scientists who work with stem cells might need to work during the weekend or even in the middle of the night for some experiments but if you find your work exciting then this is not a problem. Science is a global enterprise that needs people from all around the world to work together; it is the scientists who love what they do and collaborate with each other that are the most successful. If you think you might want to be a scientist that works with stem cells then start by doing some research of your own. Find out what potential stem cells have for the future of medical science and why stem cell research can be a controversial issue.

Answered by Javier Gonzalez-Lendinez who went to school in Spain

To become a stem cell scientist in Spain and I guess in the UK as well, you should try to study different sciences at school; with a special focus on biology, of course, but not exclusively. Other sciences are also important to broaden your knowledge before making a choice for college. Moreover, as a stem cell scientist, I use everyday concepts from chemistry or maths for example, so it is important to learn those things well from school. At university, you should study a Bachelor's degree programme in a life science such as biology or biochemistry. These degrees will give you the experience to be considered a good candidate for an MSc (Res) or for a PhD in stem cell biology. Although you can also apply to become a stem cell scientist with other Bachelors, such as physics or informatics, this is more difficult and your work within the team might be different. I did biology and chemistry all through school and in the first year at university. My BSc degree was in Molecular Biology but included a lot of developmental biology which I was particularly interested in. My PhD involved the cell and molecular biology of *Drosophila* development. I then had postdoctoral jobs in liver metabolism and PDE enzymes before coming to work in a stem cell research lab. So I have changed fields a few times!

Answered by Angela McCahill who went to school in Scotland

One of the most direct routes to become a stem cell scientist would be to do biology at school, a degree in a biological science and then a higher degree such as a PhD in a lab which is doing stem cell research. However, people from different science backgrounds can end up being stem cell scientists; for example, people with medical degrees, people who started working in labs or in industry straight from school or college, people who have spent years researching a particular disease or problem and now find that stem cells are the most useful tool to use to study it.

27 August 2014

⇨ The above information is reprinted with kind permission from EuroStemCell. Please visit www.eurostemcell.org for further information.

What does the public think about stem cell research?

By James O'Malley

Stem cell research is the subject of much discussion and interest across the world. Newspapers frequently report new discoveries, and this fast-paced field has been the focus of hope, hype and sometimes controversy. Policy makers, regulators, clinicians and scientists are constantly debating the progress and potential applications of this exciting science. But all of us may be affected by the changes in medicine that this research could bring about. Members of the public are vitally important stakeholders – so what do we all really think about stem cells? We've collected below a list of some of the most recent research carried out with members of the public in different regions of the world with the aim of answering this question.

EU

Eurobarometer 'Biotechnology' survey 2010

A survey carried out by the European Commission covering individuals over 15 years old in each of the member states of the EU revealed:

⇨ 80% of EU citizens supported embryonic stem cell research (up from 53% in 2005)

⇨ 84% supported non-embryonic stem cell research (c.g. adult/tissue stem cells)

⇨ 67% supported research with human embryonic stem cells (up from 41% in 2005).

In response to the statement: 'Research involving human embryos should be forbidden, even if this means possible treatments are not available to ill people', it was found that:

⇨ 50% did not support a ban on human embryonic stem cell research (39% for, 12% don't know/no response).

Read the full reports:

⇨ Special Eurobarometer 341, 'Biotechnology', European Commission, 2010 (pdf)

⇨ Eurobarometer64.3, 'Europeans and Biotechnology', European Commission, 2005 (pdf)

Germany

A telephone survey of 1,006 German citizens on the theme of 'Stem Cell Research' was carried out by the market and social research institute TNS Emnid on behalf of the Stem Cell Network North Rhine Westphalia from 2013. Key findings included:

⇨ 92,5% of respondents aware of stem cells

⇨ 78% opposed to a ban on stem cell research

⇨ 73.8% support increased funding for stem cell research

⇨ 83.5% support use of stem cells to treat patients

⇨ 67.8% support use of tissue stem cells for research

⇨ 50.5% support use of embryonic stem cells for research.

Read more about this research:

⇨ EuroStemCell article summarising the survey findings in more detail

⇨ The full report on the survey can be found (in German) in the 2013 issue of the *Jahrbuch für Wissenschaft und Ethik*, 22–23 January

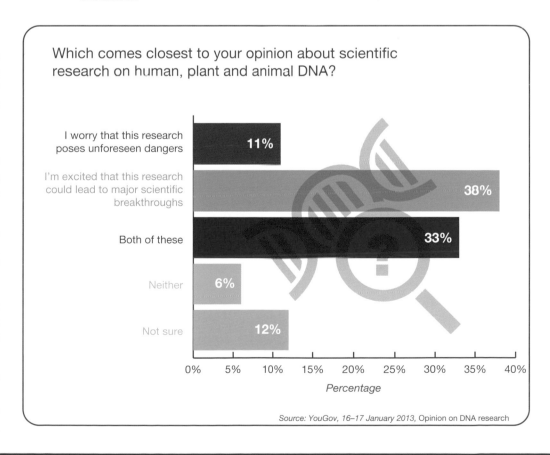

Which comes closest to your opinion about scientific research on human, plant and animal DNA?

- I worry that this research poses unforeseen dangers: **11%**
- I'm excited that this research could lead to major scientific breakthroughs: **38%**
- Both of these: **33%**
- Neither: **6%**
- Not sure: **12%**

Percentage

Source: YouGov, 16–17 January 2013, Opinion on DNA research

UK

Public Attitudes to Science survey 2014

A survey carried out on over 1,700 UK adults aged 16+, conducted on behalf of the UK Government, identified:

⇨ 57% of UK citizens feel the benefits of stem cell research outweigh any potential risks

⇨ 90% had heard of 'stem cells' but only 34% felt 'well-informed' about them.

Read the full report: Public Attitudes to Science, Dept. for Business, Innovation and Skills, UK Government, 2014

Wellcome Trust Monitor 2009 and 2012

A survey of both young people (age 14–18) and adults (aged 18+) in the UK was carried out on behalf of the medical research charity and funding agency the Wellcome Trust in 2009 and again in 2012. Regarding stem cells:

⇨ 26% of the adults questioned and 31% of youths had a 'very/good understanding' of stem cells

⇨ 25% of the adults questioned and 13% of youths felt they understood the potential uses of stem cells.

Read the full report: Wellcome Trust Monitor, 2009 and 2012

MRC and BBSRC Stem Cell Dialogue 2008

This study was commissioned by two scientific funding agencies; the Medical Research Council (MRC) and the Biotechnology and Biological Sciences Research Council (BBSRC). The study used a series of public workshops to explore the opinion towards stem cell research in the UK. This study reported:

⇨ 22% of participants were familiar with stem cells

⇨ 80% supported parallel research on adult and embryonic stem cells.

Read the full report: Stem Cell Dialogue, MRC and BBSRC, 2008

USA

Meta-analysis of opinion polls in USA

A study published in the peer-reviewed *New England Journal of Medicine* in 2011 reported the results of an analysis of several opinion polls on attitudes of US citizens towards embryonic stem cell research. It should be noted that different polling methods, specific questions and analysis techniques were used in the opinion polls forming the basis of this report. The authors found the following:

⇨ 62% believe medical research using human embryonic stem cells is acceptable

⇨ 60% were against a ban on embryonic stem cell research.

Read the full report (may require journal subscription): Blendon RJ, Kim MK, Benson JM. The public, political parties, and stem-cell research. *N Engl J Med* 2011;365:1853-6

VCU Life Sciences Survey 2002–2010

This telephone survey was carried out annually from 2002 to 2010 (except 2009) by the Virginia Commonwealth University (VCU). Roughly 1,000 US citizens (1,000-1,005) were polled on their opinion and support of stem cell research. An analysis of this data identified:

⇨ An increase in support for embryonic stem cell research from 40% (2002) to 65% (2010).

Read the full analysis: Nisbet M and Markowitz EM, (2014) Understanding Public Opinion in Debates over Biomedical Research: Looking beyond Political Partisanship to Focus on Beliefs about Science and Society. *PLoS ONE* 9(2)

Worldwide

BBVA Foundation study on Biotechnology

In 2008, the BBVA Foundation, an organisation that promotes research, training and communication of science, carried out a survey in a number of countries in western Europe as well as the USA, Japan and Israel. This face-to-face survey was carried out among 1,500 people in each participating country, and revealed:

⇨ Globally there is a great disparity in awareness of stem cells – from 33% (Japan) to 86% (Sweden, Denmark) of respondents having heard of stem cells

⇨ There is a broad consensus that stem cell research is useful

⇨ Opinion was divided when it came to prioritising medical benefits over the rights of the embryo: people in six countries were overall pro-medical, people in seven countries were more pro-embryo and the public in two countries gave medical benefits and protection of the embryo equal priority

⇨ Acceptance of human embryonic stem cell research was higher when potential medical benefits were made clear to respondents

⇨ Across all countries, acceptance was higher for the use of human embryos leftover from fertility treatments, than for the use of embryos created specifically for research

Read the full report: Fundación BBVA, Second BBVA Foundation International Study on Biotechnology, *Attitudes to Stem Cell Research and Hybrid Embryos*, May 2008 (pdf)

Last updated: 31 March 2014

⇨ The above information is reprinted with kind permission from EuroStemCell. Please visit www.eurostemcell.org for further information.

© Copyright 2008-2015
EuroStemCell

Embryonic stem cell research: an ethical dilemma

Embryonic stem cells offer hope for new therapies, but their use in research has been hotly debated. Different countries have chosen to regulate embryonic stem cell research in very different ways. Mention embryonic stem cells in the pub and the topic still divides opinion. But what exactly are the ethical arguments and why are they so tricky to resolve?

The ethical dilemma

Embryonic stem cell research poses a moral dilemma. It forces us to choose between two moral principles:

⇨ The duty to prevent or alleviate suffering

⇨ The duty to respect the value of human life.

In the case of embryonic stem cell research, it is impossible to respect both moral principles. To obtain embryonic stem cells, the early embryo has to be destroyed. This means destroying a potential human life. But embryonic stem cell research could lead to the discovery of new medical treatments that would alleviate the suffering of many people. So which moral principle should have the upper hand in this situation? The answer hinges on how we view the embryo. Does it have the status of a person?

What moral status does the human embryo have?

The moral status of the embryo is a controversial and complex issue. The main viewpoints are outlined below.

1. The embryo has full moral status from fertilisation onwards

Either the embryo is viewed as a person whilst it is still an embryo, or it is seen as a potential person. The criteria for 'personhood' are notoriously unclear; different people define what makes a person in different ways.

Arguments for this view

Development from a fertilised egg into a baby is a continuous process and any attempt to pinpoint when personhood begins is arbitrary. A human embryo is a human being in the embryonic stage, just as an infant is a human being in the infant stage. Although an embryo does not currently have the characteristics of a person, it will become a person and should be given the respect and dignity of a person.

Arguments against this view

An early embryo that has not yet implanted into the uterus does not have the psychological, emotional or physical properties that we associate with being a person. It therefore does not have any interests to be protected and we can use it for the benefit of patients (who ARE persons).

The embryo cannot develop into a child without being transferred to a woman's uterus. It needs external help to develop. Even then, the probability that embryos used for *in vitro* fertilisation will develop into full-term successful births is low. Something that could potentially become a person should not be treated as if it actually were a person.

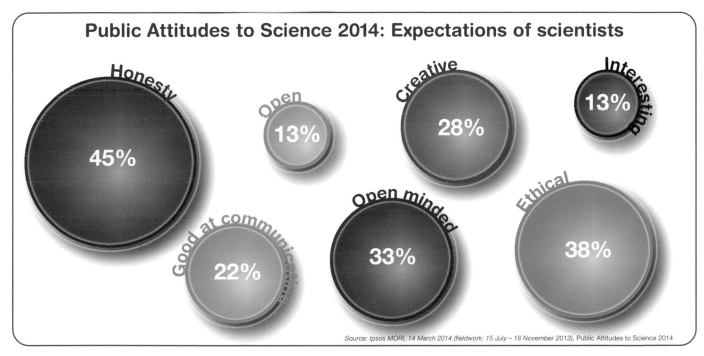

Public Attitudes to Science 2014: Expectations of scientists

Honesty **45%**

Open **13%**

Creative **28%**

Interesting **13%**

Good at communicating **22%**

Open minded **33%**

Ethical **38%**

Source: Ipsos MORI, 14 March 2014 (fieldwork: 15 July – 18 November 2013), Public Attitudes to Science 2014

2. There is a cut-off point at 14 days after fertilisation

Some people argue that a human embryo deserves special protection from around day 14 after fertilisation because:

⇨ After 14 days the embryo can no longer split to form twins. Before this point, the embryo could still be split to become two or more babies, or it might fail to develop at all.

⇨ Before day 14, the embryo has no central nervous system and therefore no senses. If we can take organs from patients who have been declared brain dead and use them for transplants, then we can also use hundred-cell embryos that have no nervous system.

⇨ Fertilisation is itself a process, not a 'moment'. An embryo in the earliest stages is not clearly defined as an individual.

3. The embryo has increasing status as it develops

An embryo deserves some protection from the moment the sperm fertilises the egg, and its moral status increases as it becomes more human-like.

Arguments for this view

There are several stages of development that could be given increasing moral status:

1. Implantation of the embryo into the uterus wall around six days after fertilisation.

2. Appearance of the primitive streak – the beginnings of the nervous system – at around 14 days.

3. The phase when the baby could survive if born prematurely.

4. Birth.

If a life is lost, we tend to feel differently about it depending on the stage of the lost life. A fertilised egg before implantation in the uterus could be granted a lesser degree of respect than a human foetus or a born baby.

More than half of all fertilised eggs are lost due to natural causes. If the natural process involves such loss, then using some embryos in stem cell research should not worry us either.

Arguments against this view

We protect a person's life and interests not because they are valuable from the point of view of the universe, but because they are important to the person concerned. Whatever moral status the human embryo has for us, the life that it lives has a value to the embryo itself.

If we judge the moral status of the embryo from its age, then we are making arbitrary decisions about who is human. For example, even if we say formation of the nervous system marks the start of personhood, we still would not say a patient who has lost nerve cells in a stroke has become less human.

If we are not sure whether a fertilized egg should be considered a human being, then we should not destroy it. A hunter does not shoot if he is not sure whether his target is a deer or a man.

4. The embryo has no moral status at all

An embryo is organic material with a status no different from other body parts.

Arguments for this view

Fertilised human eggs are just parts of other people's bodies until they have developed enough to survive independently. The only respect due to blastocysts is the respect that should be shown to other people's property. If we destroy a blastocyst before implantation into the uterus we do not harm it because it has no beliefs, desires, expectations, aims or purposes to be harmed.

Arguments against this view

By taking embryonic stem cells out of an early embryo, we prevent the embryo from developing in its normal way. This means it is prevented from becoming what it was programmed to become – a human being.

Embryonic stem cell research and religion

Different religions view the status of the early human embryo in different ways. For example, the Roman Catholic, Orthodox and conservative Protestant Churches believe the embryo has the status of a human from conception and no embryo research should be permitted. Judaism and Islam emphasise the importance of helping others and argue that the embryo does not have full human status before 40 days, so both these religions permit some research on embryos. Other religions take other positions. You can read more about this by downloading the extended version of this factsheet at the address below.

Acknowledgements and references

This factsheet was created by Kristina Hug and reviewed by Göran Hermerén.

23 March 2011

⇨ The above information is reprinted with kind permission from EuroStemCell. Please visit www.eurostemcell.org for further information.

Human cloning first: stem cells created from adult skin cells

Appeared in BioNews 751.

By Sarah Guy

Scientists have used a cloning technique to successfully create human embryonic stem cells from adult cells for the first time.

The technique has worked previously using cells from babies, but it was thought that the natural mutations that occur as they age would mean that it could not be achieved using adult cells. But the researchers had success using skin cells from a 35-year-old man and a 75-year-old man.

The research team removed the nucleus from an egg cell and replaced it with the nucleus of an adult skin cell in a process called somatic cell nuclear transfer (SCNT). SCNT is the process that was used to create Dolly the sheep in 1996.

After shocking the cells with electricity, they began dividing until they formed a ball of a few hundred cells – a blastocyst – which has the potential to be grown into a number of different tissue types. These tissues could one day be used to treat a range of disorders including Parkinson's disease, heart disease and even spinal cord injuries.

'Therapeutic cloning has long been envisioned as a means for generating patient-specific stem cells that could be used to treat a range of age-related diseases.' said Dr Robert Lanza, a co-author of the study, from Advanced Cell Technology [has since changed name to Ocata Therapeutics] in Massachusetts, USA.

'However, despite cloning success in animals, the derivation of stem cells from cloned human embryos has proven elusive. Only one group has ever succeeded, and their lines were generated using foetal and infant cells', he added.

Professor Shoukhrat Mitalipov, from Oregon Health and Science University, who developed the technique, said: 'The advance here is showing that (nuclear transfer) looks like it will work with people of all ages. I'm happy to hear that our experiment was verified and shown to be genuine'.

There are ethical concerns regarding the team's discovery, however. While the blastocysts created by the current research would never give rise to a human embryo, the findings raise the prospect of using a similar technique to create a cloned embryo. Dr Lanza recognises the risk of attempting to do this, remarking that it would be 'unsafe and grossly unethical' to NBC News.

Meanwhile, one of Dr Lanza's colleagues, Dong-ryul Lee, from CHA University in South Korea, has found that only relatively few human stem cell lines are needed to be able to treat numerous people without fear of immunorejection.

Lee and his colleagues discovered that 28 types of human embryonic stem cells developed in South Korea can be transplanted into up to a quarter of Koreans without being rejected by the body. This means theoretically that just 100 to 160 stem cell lines would need to be generated in order to treat the whole of the South Korean population, they suggest.

The research was published in Cell Stem Cell.

28 April 2014

⇨ The above information is reprinted with kind permission from BioNews. Please visit www.bionews.org.uk for further information.

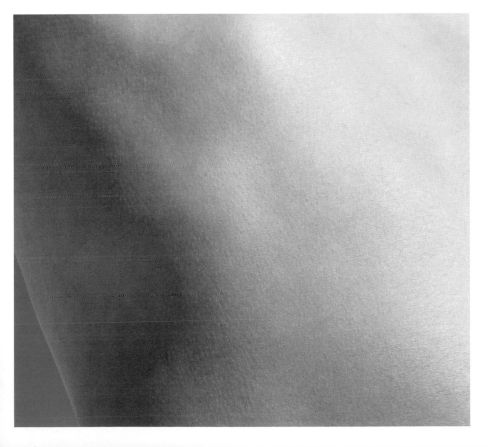

Will human cloning be available by 2030?

By Alice

Should humans be cloned? That is the question that many people all over the world have been debating for a long time now even though scientists have proved a number of times that human cloning could be highly beneficial to the human race, if it were legal.

Introduction

Some say that the idea of human cloning is morally wrong and that we would be 'Playing God'. However, facts show that there is nothing physically wrong with human cloning. If the law allowed human cloning, it would not only save lives, but it would lead to a number of advancements in scientific research, and improve the quality of life. Especially of those parents who are infertile or have once before lost a loved one. The possibility of human cloning was raised when Scottish scientists at Roslin Institute created the cloned sheep 'Dolly'. This attracted a lot of attention for its scientific advancement and its ethical problems.

Will the science be ready?

Scientists have been cloning animals for many years. In 1952, the first animal, a tadpole, was cloned. Since Dolly the sheep, researchers have cloned a number of large and small animals including sheep, goats, cows, mice, pigs, cats, rabbits, and a gaur and all these clones were created using nuclear transfer technology. This technology involves an egg cell, with its nucleus removed, instead implanted with the DNA from a donor cell. This egg then has to be treated with chemicals or an electric current to stimulate cell division and once the cloned embryo reaches a suitable stage, it is then transferred to the womb of a surrogate mother, where it develops as normal until birth. A clone created using nuclear transfer technology is not truly identical to the donor animal; this is because only the clone's chromosomes are the same as the donor. Some of the clone's genetic materials come from the mitochondria in the cytoplasm of the egg.

Already hundreds of cloned animals exist today, but the number of different species is limited as attempts at cloning certain species have been unsuccessful. This could be because some species may be more resistant to the nuclear transfer than others, and the process of extracting the nucleus from an egg cell and replacing it with the nucleus of a donor cell is a traumatic one, and improvements in cloning technologies may be needed before other species can be cloned successfully. If cloning technology does work then we will almost certainly be able to clone the dead too, from cells taken from their bodies before they die and kept alive in culture. This is a very standard technique and using this technique parents could 'reproduce' an exact copy of a child who tragically died, and also Dolly the sheep was made using frozen cells. A recent claim from Clonaid states that in January 2003 they had cloned the dead son of a Japanese couple who had been killed in an accident. This shows us that the science involved in making human clones is not far off, as the speed at which scientists are making developments in genetics is very rapid.

In any case there could be a less risky type of cloning, which would be therapeutic cloning, this can be used to make tissues and organs for transplants. To do this, DNA would be extracted from the person in need of a transplant and inserted into an empty egg. After the egg containing the patient's DNA starts to divide, embryonic stem cells would be harvested. The stem cells would be used to form an organ or tissue that is a genetic match to the recipient. And so in theory, the cloned organ could then be transplanted into the patient without the risk of tissue rejection. If organs could be generated from cloned human embryos, the need for organ donation could be significantly reduced.

Many challenges must be overcome before these transplants could become reality, such like the full human cloning. More effective technologies for creating human embryos, harvesting stem cells, and producing organs from stem cells would have to be developed. In 2001, the first human embryos were cloned; however, the only embryo to survive the cloning process stopped developing after diving into six cells. Then in February 2002, scientists with the same technology reported that they had successfully transplanted kidney-like organs into cows. The team of researchers created a cloned cow embryo by removing the DNA from an egg cell and then injecting the DNA from the skin cell of the donor cow's ear. Since little is known about manipulating embryonic stem cells from cows, the scientists let the cloned embryos develop into foetuses. The scientists then harvested foetal tissue from the clones and transplanted it into the donor cow. In the three months of observation following the transplant, no sign of immune rejection was observed in the transplant recipient.

But human cloning does have some large risks, mainly health risks, towards the cloned baby/embryo. There are huge risks of mutations, which may not be able to be picked up by gene testing or ultrasound scans until after the birth. Problems also may arise due to errors in the genetic material from the donor cell. Defects in the genes of the DNA from a single donor cell may lead to developmental abnormalities in cloned embryos. In addition, scientists do not know how cloning could impact mental development, While factors such as intellect and mood may not be as important for a cow or a mouse, they are crucial for the development of healthy humans.

Also reproductive cloning is expensive and highly inefficient. More than 90% of cloning attempts fail to produce healthy embryos and more than 100 nuclear transfer procedures could be required to produce one healthy clone. In addition to low success rates, cloned animals tend to have more compromised immune function and higher rates of infection, tumour growth and other disorders, as many studies have shown, such as: in Japan, cloned mice live in poor health and die early, about a third of the cloned calves born alive have died young, and many of them were abnormally large. But many cloned animals have not lived long enough to generate valid data about how clones age as appearing healthy at a young age is not a good indicator of long-term survival. Clones have also been known to die for no obvious reason; for example, Australia's first cloned sheep appeared healthy and energetic on the day she died, and the results from her autopsy failed to determine a cause of death. Even some scientists believe today's technology just isn't ready to be tested on humans. Ian Wilmut, one of Dolly's co-creators, has said that human cloning projects would be irresponsible. Cloning technology is still in its early stages, and nearly 98 per cent of cloning efforts end in failure. The embryos are either not suitable for implanting into the uterus, or die some time during growth or shortly after birth.

Those clones that do survive suffer from genetic abnormalities. Clone cells may age more rapidly, shortening their lifespan, similar to what happened with Dolly. Some clones have been born with defective hearts, lung problems, diabetes, blood vessel complications and malfunctioning immune systems. One of the more famous cases involved a cloned sheep that was born but suffered from chronic hyperventilation caused by malformed arteries leading to the lungs.

Will it be ethically and socially accepted?

Due to the inefficiency of animal cloning and the lack of understanding about reproductive cloning, many scientists strongly believe that it would be unethical to attempt to clone humans. Not only do most attempts to clone mammals fail but about 30% of clones born alive are affected with 'large-offspring syndrome' and other debilitating conditions and these same problems would be expected in human cloning. With so many unknowns around reproductive cloning, the attempt to clone humans at this time is considered potentially dangerous and ethically irresponsible.

Surveys have shown that few approve of cloning for reproductive purposes, although more are open to therapeutic cloning. Also the US Government has hindered the development of human cloning technologies by, firstly, not funding research focused on human cloning for reproduction. Also, the FDA, which regulates public cloning research, requires anyone in the United States attempting to clone humans to first get its permission.

Certain countries abroad have stricter standards, and more than 50 have legally banned research efforts on reproductive human cloning. In Japan, human cloning is a crime punishable by up to ten years in prison and here in England scientists have been allowed to clone human embryos for therapeutic use only.

It has been pointed out, that while defective clones in other animals may not pose any worry, it becomes ethically and morally wrong to risk this happening during the human cloning process. This has led to the response that it's now easier to pick out defective embryos before they're implanted into the mother. In 2005, the United Nations attempted to pass a global ban on human cloning, but was unsuccessful due to disagreements over whether therapeutic cloning should be included. For now, human cloning remains in a troubling position from both a scientific and a public policy perspective.

The cloning of a human, holds many social and emotional risks, for example – a child grows up knowing her mother is in fact her sister, her grandmother is actually her mother. Every time her mother looks at her she is seeing herself growing up. These can pose unbearable emotional pressures on a teenager trying to establish his or her identity.

What happens to a marriage when the 'father' sees his wife's clone grow up into the exact replica by appearance, of the 18-year-old he fell in love with 35 years ago? A sexual relationship would of course be with his wife's twin, so no incest involved technically.

But at the same time, human cloning could be used to improve the quality of life, you could recover someone who was loved and have them in your life once more. But here more problems could be caused, as this person may not end up being the same, personality wise, and would also grow up during a different generation.

Infertility could be treated; rather than use donated sperm and eggs, why not use a cell of your own to give birth to 'yourself'?

In conclusion, even after more than a decade since Dolly, human cloning remains in its infancy. Although cloning technology has improved, the process still has a slim success rate of one to four per cent. That being said, science is headed in the direction of those success rates increasing. Whether clones will be ready by 2030, also depends on the loosening of the governmental restraints involving human cloning and also the public view; which at the moment appears to be a very closed 'no', as most people see human cloning as a violation against God, or an unnecessary movement which could be emotionally wrecking to the clones. Although the idea of human cloning being available is a widely spread answer, as different countries around the world may have different views and different stages of the technology. For example, places like the UK, America and China may have the technology readily available, but the idea would still be pushed aside because of the social and ethical problems human cloning poses. On the other hand, some less developed countries, may not have the technology to hand, but if that technology were obtained then the ethical argument may not be such a weighted factor and human cloning could in fact occur.

References:

1. This site was modified in 2009, meaning that its relevance is still pretty high as this was only a few years ago. But the rate at which technology concerning human cloning has advanced could see this article as out of date. But for the purposes of the methods undertaken, this site is still suitable and gives valid information.

2. Kevin Bonsor is a freelance writer. He holds a bachelor's degree in journalism from Georgia Southern University.

As a writer and blogger for HowStuffWorks and a contributing writer for Discovery News, Cristen specialises in technology and the science of everyday living. Her articles have featured on Huffington Post, ABC Science and MSNBC. com. Both these authors seem like a valid source, having written articles featured on science pieces.

3. Again a page last updated in 2009, and so should still be up to date with the current affairs and ethical issues on human cloning, the site also states 'We will attempt to overcome our biases on each topic that we describe, by explaining each point of view carefully, respectfully and objectively. To this end, we have many of our essays reviewed by persons familiar with the issues who represent all sides of each topic.' Giving me confidence that it is also an unbiased source of information.

4. Written by the author Patrick Dixon, I found more than 500,000 web pages talk about Patrick Dixon and his ideas, with cumulative TV, radio and press audience reach estimated to be more than 450 million. He has been ranked one of the 20 most influential business thinkers alive today. So his research and views given may not be completely unbiased, but they give a lot of information in the many different areas of human cloning, giving alternatives for the use of the cloning technology. And ethical and social reasons people may not be willing to let human cloning happen.

5. Written by a science editor, around 2009. Written in *The Telegraph* newspaper within the 'science' section. This piece is a valid unbiased piece, having being produced by a science editor who understands the science and can portray it in a non-biased way.

2 February 2014

⇨ The above information is reprinted with kind permission from Tutor Hunt. Please visit www.tutorhunt.com for further information.

Mini glossary

Eugenics – an attempt to improve the human race.

Megalomania – a desire to reproduce one's own qualities.

Organ donors – healthy humans could be cloned en masse to then solve the problem of the lack or organ donors.

Spare parts – using a cell from your own body to duplicate yourself. Then take tissue, e.g. bone marrow which you could use to get cured from many diseases and disorders, then offer baby for adoption.

Compassion objects to cloning farm animals

Compassion is deeply concerned by news reports that BGI (Beijing Genomics Institute) is cloning pigs on an industrial scale in China.

Reportedly, scientists are cloning pigs in order to test new medicines. BGI is the world's largest centre for cloning pigs, as well as the world's largest centre for gene sequencing.

BGI's chief executive Wang Jun reportedly said 'If it tastes good you should sequence it.'

BGI is investigating the genes of animals for industrial use – for example by increasing yields – the amount of piglets a sow can produce.

Compassion is against cloning animals for food production because cloning entails serious health and welfare issues for animals. There is an increased risk of problematic births when surrogate mothers are carrying cloned offspring. Furthermore, many cloned animals die premature deaths as they have a higher mortality rate than non-cloned animals.

The European Commission has recently proposed new legislation on cloning animals for food production. It suggests that cloning of farm animals and the sale of meat and milk from these animals should be banned. However, the Commission has not extended this ban to the offspring of clones. In addition, meat or milk from the offspring of clones would not have to be labelled, so consumers would not know whether cloning was involved in the food they were buying.

Peter Stevenson, Compassion's Chief Policy Advisor, says 'The cloning of farm animals risks perpetuating industrial farming. Clones and their offspring are likely to have very high yields and growth rates leaving them vulnerable to damaging health problems. Cloning is out of step with the growing recognition of the need to respect animals as sentient beings.'

Compassion is presenting its objections to the European Parliament. We are calling for a ban on the use of the offspring of clones in EU farming and on the sale of food from the offspring of clones.

15 January 2014

⇨ The above information is reprinted with kind permission from Compassion in World Farming. Please visit www.ciwf.org.uk for further information.

Cloned animals

Foods produced from cloned animals fall under Regulation (EC) No 258/97 (the 'Novel Foods Regulation'). This means that meat, milk or eggs from cloned animals would be subjected to a safety evaluation and approved by all European Union (EU) member states as a novel food before they could be marketed legally.

Assessing new food technologies

The Food Standards Agency is the UK body responsible for the assessment of novel foods and it will not assess the safety of using cloned animals and their offspring in the food chain unless it is asked to do so. If a company wants authorisation to market food produced using cloned animals, then the Agency is obliged to assess the food safety implications.

During any such safety assessment, the Agency will consult an independent advisory committee, the Advisory Committee on Novel Foods and Processes (ACNFP). The ACNFP comprises experts who advise the Agency on a wide range of new foods and food technologies.

The Agency is aware that the use of cloned animals in the food chain has been examined by the authorities in the US, which announced in January 2008 that edible products from cloned cattle, pigs and goats are as safe as their conventional counterparts. As a result, some US producers could start to use cloned animals or, more likely, the offspring of cloned animals. This may lead to the technology being considered for use in Europe.

Seeking views from the public

In advance of the possibility of being asked to consider the safety of food produced from cloned animals, the FSA carried out research in 2008 to help understand the views of the UK public about this technology and about cloned animals, their offspring and their products (such as milk and eggs) entering the UK food chain.

The key areas of concern raised by people were food safety, consumer benefits, animal welfare and trust. The research report concluded that the general public would only accept the idea of buying and eating food derived from clones and their offspring if each of these concerns has been addressed.

The findings from this research will enable the views of the UK public to be reflected in any EU discussions about the use of the technology.

The summary report of findings can be found at the address given at the end of this article.

Concerns about animal welfare and agricultural practices are not dealt with by the Agency. These are the responsibility of the Department for Environment, Food & Rural Affairs (Defra).

What is cloning?

Cloning is the creation of an organism (the clone) that is an exact genetic copy of another organism (the donor).

Clones occur in nature and many plants, such as strawberries, propagate in this way. Some animals also clone themselves, such as amoeba (a microscopic single-celled organism) and some insects, such as greenfly. Cloning sometimes occurs in humans too – identical twins can be thought of as clones as they share exactly the same genetic material (although strictly speaking neither one is a copy of the other).

Cloning is widely used in horticulture, as plants grown from a cutting or a graft are genetic copies of the original plants, and some foods that we eat, such as potatoes, bananas and grapes are derived from clones.

Clones of cattle and other farm animals can be produced using a technique known as somatic cell nuclear transfer (SCNT). SCNT was first used successfully in sheep to produce 'Dolly' at the Roslin Institute in 1996. SCNT does not occur naturally.

'Novel' status of food from descendants of cloned cattle and pigs

At its meeting in December 2010, the FSA Board made clear its position that the marketing of products obtained from cloned animals should continue to be subject to the Novel Foods Regulation (Regulation (EC) No 258/97), and require authorisation. However, based on the available evidence, the Board agreed that there are no food safety grounds for regulating food such as meat and milk from the descendants of cloned cattle and pigs.

The Agency subsequently sought the views of interested parties on this potential change in the interpretation of the regulation in respect of food from the descendants of cloned cattle and pigs.

The majority of responses received by the FSA did not address the specific question regarding the scope of the regulation but raised various concerns about food safety, animal welfare and ethics. Although some specific questions, including whether the Agency should take factors other than food safety into account when assessing novel foods, were raised and considered by the Agency, none of the responses received were viewed to change the overall conclusion reached by the Board.

In view of this, the FSA announced on 13 May 2011 that it had changed its advice on the scope of the novel foods regulation in relation to the descendants of cloned cattle and pigs. In doing so, the FSA indicated that it will investigate what further steps might be taken in light of the continuing consumer concerns over ethical issues in relation to food from cloned animals or their descendants.

Change.org petition: 'Food from offspring of cloned animals should be labelled'

The Food Standards Agency response to the December 2010 petition raised on the website change.org can be found here: http://www.food.gov.uk/sites/default/files/multimedia/pdfs/petitionresponsejan2011.pdf.

⇨ The above information is reprinted with kind permission from Food Standards Agency. Please visit www.food.gov.uk for further information.

© Crown copyright 2015

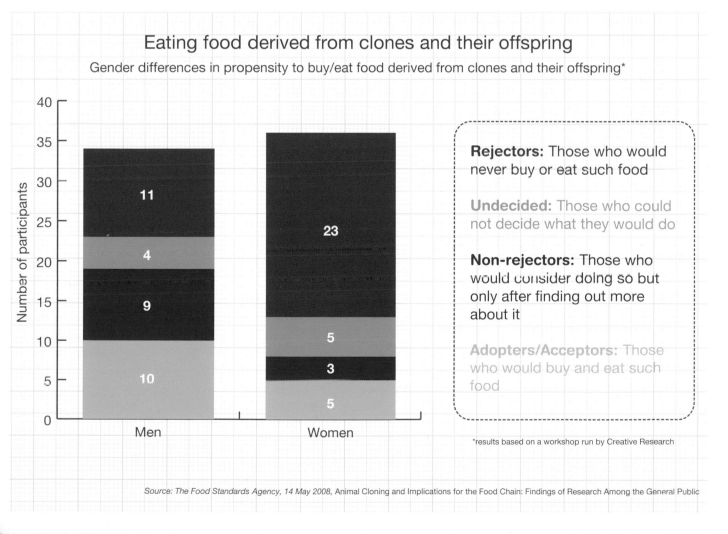

Eating food derived from clones and their offspring

Gender differences in propensity to buy/eat food derived from clones and their offspring*

Rejectors: Those who would never buy or eat such food

Undecided: Those who could not decide what they would do

Non-rejectors: Those who would consider doing so but only after finding out more about it

Adopters/Acceptors: Those who would buy and eat such food

*results based on a workshop run by Creative Research

Source: *The Food Standards Agency, 14 May 2008,* Animal Cloning and Implications for the Food Chain: Findings of Research Among the General Public

Is cloned meat the answer to IPCC's climate change food shortage?

By Susanne Posel

The World Bank (WB) is warning that climate change will affect urban populations by constricting the amount of food (including meat from livestock) that can be utilised.

Farmland used to raise livestock will become less of a luxury as sources of protein are decreased and the manufacturing of food sources remains un-ecofriendly.

Rachel Kyte, vice president of the WB commented: 'The challenges from waste to warming, spurred on by a growing population with a rising middle-class hunger for meat, are leading us down a dangerous path.'

Kyte continues: 'Without significant change this could drastically affect our world – if there even is a world left to enjoy. Unless we chart a new course, we will find ourselves staring volatility and disruption in the food system in the face; not in 2050, not in 2040, but potentially within the next decade.'

Indeed, the report Kyte is basing her comments on comes from the UN Intergovernmental Panel on Climate Change (IPCC) which states that because of global warming the reduced grain production observed in recent years will rise to its height in a few years and remain at unprecedented levels for the next 800,000 years.

The report is purported to provide policymakers with a scientific foundation to tackle the challenge of climate change. It would help governments and other stakeholders work together at various levels, including a new international agreement to limit climate change that countries intend to broker by the end of next year.

Dr Rajendra Pachauri, chair of the UN IPCC said in 2007 that human populations globally should reduce their meat consumption by having a meat-free day once per week to reduce greenhouse gases.

The UN Food and Agricultural Organization (UNFAO) have reported that 18% of the world's greenhouse gases and CO_2 equivalents can be directly contributed to livestock. If we had less animals raised for consumption, we could cull considerable environmental benefits.

Another study published by *Environmental Research Letters* claims that there must be drastic changes in food production by 2050 to prevent a global food crisis due to global warming.

Another proposed answer to the problem of livestock cultivation is adopting a global vegetarian diet, the world's water supplies will be saved and the erratic weather evidenced by the man-made climate change myth will simply disappear. Miraculously, third world nations would have the arable land to feed their populations, which would increase trade and food surplus.

S. Matthew Laio, bioethics professor at New York University proposed that the masses take a pill that would cause nausea when a person ate meat. This would eventually create a lasting aversion to meat-eating.

Another solution to replacing livestock is the creation of artificial meat.

Researchers in the laboratory are creating synthetic (or test tube meat) that may make an appearance on supermarket shelves. By taking cells from a living animal, then 'growing' it in a Petri dish, the theory is that this concoction of animal tissue can be consumed by humans.

Gabor Forgacs, tissue engineer at the University of Missouri has been developing organ replacement technology. This breakthrough could be used to engineer test tube meat for human consumption.

Test tube meat, being a possible answer to the cultivation of livestock, produces 78–96% less CO2, according to the EU and research from the University of Oxford.

Tom Vislack, secretary of the U.S. Department of Agriculture (USDA) admitted that the agency cannot determine whether or not cloned meat has been sold in the US.

The USDA has decided to tell the American public that cloned meat is safe for consumption. Vilsack remarked that cloned meat has no 'substantial difference to actual animal meat, and therefore it is safe'.

Vislack said : 'I can't say today that I can answer your question in an affirmative or negative way. I don't know. What I do know is that we know all the research, all of the review of this is suggested that this is safe.'

27 August 2014

⇨ The above information is reprinted with kind permission from author Susanne Posel and Foundation Media, LLC. Please visit http://occupycorporatism.com for further information.

Making the food and farming industry more competitive while protecting the environment

Cloning of farmed animals

Cloning is the creation of an organism that is an almost exact genetic copy of another.

Cloned animals and food safety

The Government agrees with the European Food Safety Authority (EFSA) that there is no evidence of any difference in the safety of food produced from cloned animals or their descendants and that from conventionally bred animals.

EU developments on animal cloning for food production

The European Commission has announced proposals IP/13/1269 to prohibit the commercial cloning of animals for food production (although they will allow scientific research to continue) and to ban the sale of food produced from clones.

The UK Government believes these controls are unnecessary. Not only are there no food safety issues associated with food from clones, but existing EU and national legislation will provide the necessary safeguards for the welfare of the animals concerned. We will be making these points forcibly when the proposals are discussed in Brussels in due course.

It is important that we keep an open mind on new technologies; a point made recently in the Foresight report.

The Novel Foods Regulation

Meat and milk from cloned animals are classed as 'novel foods' under the EU Novel Foods Regulation (1997). This means they must be assessed for safety before they can be legally marketed anywhere in the EU.

The Food Standards Agency (FSA) is responsible for food safety, including food from cloned animals and their descendants.

In 2011, the FSA announced that food from an animal descended from a clone would no longer be classed as 'novel'. This is in line with policy by the EC and other EU member states.

Earlier negotiations to update the Novel Food Regulations failed. The EC will now consider when and how to restart the legal process of updating these.

Food labelling

The FSA deals with labelling in relation to food safety. Defra is responsible for labelling in relation to food standards and consumer choice. Meat and milk from the descendants of cloned animals do not need to be labelled as such, because there is no evidence that they are a risk to human health.

This was agreed by the FSA in 2010.

Defra's view is that mandatory labelling of meat or milk products derived from animals with a clone in their ancestry would be unenforceable and impractical.

Animal welfare

Animal welfare is regulated in the UK through a combination of EU and national legislation. Donor animals, surrogate mothers and clones themselves would be subject to these welfare requirements. For more information, see our policy on protecting animal welfare at https://www.gov.uk/government/policies/protecting-animal-welfare.

Further information

The National Standing Committee on Farm Animal Genetic Resources provided advice on cloning in 2010.

13 March 2015

⇨ The above information is reprinted with kind permission from Department for Environment, Food & Rural Affairs. Please visit www.gov.uk for further information.

Japanese researchers succeed in making generations of mouse clones

Using the technique that created Dolly the sheep, researchers from the RIKEN Center for Developmental Biology in Kobe, Japan have identified a way to produce healthy mouse clones that live a normal lifespan and can be sequentially cloned indefinitely.

Their study is published today in the journal *Cell Stem Cell*.

In an experiment that started in 2005, the team led by Dr Teruhiko Wakayama has used a technique called somatic cell nuclear transfer (SNCT) to produce 581 clones of one original 'donor' mouse, through 25 consecutive rounds of cloning.

SNCT is a widely used cloning technique whereby a cell nucleus containing the genetic information of the individual to be cloned is inserted into a living egg that has had its own nucleus removed. It has been used successfully in laboratory animals as well as farm animals.

However, until now, scientists hadn't been able to overcome the limitations of SNCT that resulted in low success rates and restricted the number of times mammals could be recloned. Attempts at recloning cats, pigs and mice more than two to six times had failed.

'One possible explanation for this limit on the number of recloning attempts is an accumulation of genetic or epigenetic abnormalities over successive generations' explains Dr Wakayama.

To prevent possible epigenetic changes, or modifications to DNA function that do not involve a change in the DNA itself, Wakayama and his team added trichostatin, a histone deacetylase inhibitor, to the cell culture medium. Using this technique, they increased cloning efficiency by up to six-fold.

By improving each step of the SCNT procedure, they were able to clone the mice repeatedly 25 times without seeing a reduction in the success rate. The 581 healthy mice obtained in this way were all fertile, they gave birth to healthy pups and lived a normal lifespan of about two years, similar to normally conceived mice.

> **'Researchers have identified a way to produce healthy mouse clones that live a normal lifespan and can be sequentially cloned indefinitely'**

'Our results show that there were no accumulations of epigenetic or genetic abnormalities in the mice, even after repeated cloning,' conclude the authors.

Dr Wakayama adds, 'This technique could be very useful for the large-scale production of superior-quality animals, for farming or conservation purposes.'

Dr Wakayama's work made the news in 2008 when his team created clones from the bodies of mice that had been frozen for 16 years, using SNCT.

6 March 2013

⇨ The above information is reprinted with kind permission from AlphaGalileo. Please visit www.alphagalileo.org for further information.

© AlphaGalileo 2015

Cloning in racehorses

By Carley Jo Cockrum

It's no surprise that cloning is a major controversy in agriculture. It's just as much a moral problem, as it is technical. Just like everything else, technology is advancing. But just because technology advances, does that necessarily mean everyone has to hop on board? After all, this isn't the same thing as just getting the newest iPhone. Early in August 2013, US District Court Judge Mary Lou Robinson rocked the boat after horse owner Jason Abraham and two of his companies, Abraham & Veneklasen Joint Venture and Abraham Equine Inc., filed a lawsuit against the American Quarter Horse Association (AQHA) in Amarillo, Texas because they didn't accept cloned horses' applications. The judge later ruled that the AQHA must include clones into their breed registry. Even though this case has no immediate bearings on thoroughbred racing, these decisions will set important legal precedents.

Most people in the thoroughbred industry want no part of cloning. After the Quarter Horse ruling, attention went toward the Jockey Club. They released a statement saying 'The facts involved in the AQHA cases are very different from those applicable to the registration of thoroughbreds and the decision in that case has no bearing on the rules for registering thoroughbreds. The Jockey Club, as an organisation dedicated to the improvement of thoroughbred racing and breeding, believes that the short- and long-term welfare of the sport of thoroughbred racing and the thoroughbred breed are best served by the current rules.'1 [1]Now, the Jockey Club makes it pretty clear that they are against competition clones. But let's not forget that AQHA has the same bans on clones, but the Texas court ruled that the quarter horse organisation was violating antimonopoly laws by banning the cloned animals. For now, the Jockey Club is in the clear and their ban is still in place; but, because of the legal precedents that the Texas case has set, if someone wanted to sue the Jockey Club, they'd have a strong case.

Cloned horses are allowed in a range of competitions. They were allowed in the 2012 Olympics, the pari-mutual mule races held at Northern California fair racetracks, and thoroughbreds have competed in the show jumping field. In an ESPN special, Bill Finely paints the picture of the 2033 Kentucky Derby being like something straight out of a science fiction novel. Kathleen McNulty, replica farm owner, does not believe that is the case, 'We don't see this as something where someone is going to create 20 copies of a famous horse and pit them against one another. There really wouldn't be a good reason to do that.'[1] While digging deeper, that seems to be a tentatively common argument amongst people for cloning.

I don't think cloning is all bad, it has plenty of pros. It can give horses who can't reproduce a chance to pass on their genes. After all, clones are able to reproduce naturally. I can understand reasons like this. However, I just can't seem to get away from the fact that in my opinion, the cons outweigh the pros. Clones commonly are subjected to birth defects, disease, and premature death.[2] Aside from just the health issues, take a second to think about how much it costs to clone. The average cost to clone a horse is around US$150,000. Not only is it expensive and dangerous, consider how it could affect society's moral standards and integrity. Allowing scientific advantages to lead the way with all of its advances with the technology to 'fix' every flaw, and make everything perfect, modern science is contradicting the natural science of the evolution of a species. If we get used to having the option of expecting only the best existing form of an animal, we aren't allowing the species to improve or exist naturally.

Every competitive horse person knows that you can buy the best horse, but should creating a champion in a test tube be considered a fair alternative?

⇨ The above information is reprinted with kind permission from SLO Horse News. Please visit www.slohorsenews.net for further information.

1 http://espn.go.com/horse-racing/story/_/id/9582361/the-sport-kings-clones

2 http://www.ehow.com/info_8536886_pros-cons-horse-cloning.html

Animal rights groups slam cloning of British dog, Winnie the dachshund

By Charlotte Meredith

Britain's first cloned dog has been born after a £60,000 test tube procedure.

The tiny dachshund puppy, weighing just over 1lb (454g), was born in Seoul, South Korea, at the end of last month following a competition advertised in the UK offering the procedure free of charge.

The dog was copied from a 12-year-old pet called Winnie, owned by Rebecca Smith, a cook from west London.

But animal rights groups have condemned the move.

The animal welfare charity Peta told the Huffington Post UK the focus should be on rehoming abandoned animals, before unnecessarily cloning them.

'Companion animal guardians should consider, instead, how their money might actually help dogs still on this Earth.

Every year, millions of homeless animals are euthanised because of a lack of suitable homes. More unfortunate animals are abandoned to fend for themselves on the streets and are often subjected to cruelty or succumb to starvation, diseases or injuries.

'Although it's understandable that some people fantasise about replicating an adored dog or cat, even if it's successful, cloning can only replicate genetic material.

'Just as fraternal twins are different people, so, too, will cloned animals develop different personalities.

'We cannot resurrect animals, but we can give living animals in desperate need a chance at a happy life.'

But the company that carried out the procedure, Sooam Biotech, has already created more than 500 cloned dogs for owners around the world.

'Mini Winnie' is thought to be the first British dog to be cloned.

The development comes after researchers at the Roslin Institute in Edinburgh produced Dolly the Sheep, the first mammal to be cloned from an adult in 1996.

Professor Sir Ian Wilmut, who led the Dolly team, told the programme that he believed owners 'might be disappointed' by dog cloning.

'I think that the owners might be disappointed – so much of the personality of a dog probably comes from the way that you treat it,' he said.

'I think that you would treat a cloned dog, particularly if you had spent 100,000 dollars, differently, so the dog would be different.

'I am sufficiently sceptical that I personally would not have a dog cloned.'

Elaine Pendlebury, senior veterinary surgeon for the PDSA charity, said in a statement that they believed cloning was 'not an appropriate way' to deal with the loss of a pet.

'We understand that losing a beloved pet is extremely upsetting, and it is important for owners to come to terms with their bereavement over time. Pets are a huge part of family life, providing love and companionship, and the void that can be left can be hard to come to terms with,' she said.

'At PDSA we provide support and advice to owners to help them deal with their feelings and come to terms with their loss. We believe that cloning is not an appropriate way to deal with the loss of a pet.

'It is important to remember that manipulating identical DNA does not lead to an identical pet. A cloned pet may look the same but their personality will be different because personality develops through life experiences, including training and socialisation.'

9 March 2015

⇨ The above information is reprinted with kind permission from Press Association. Please visit www.pressassociation. com for further information.

Mammoth cloning: the ethics

An article from The Conversation.

By Julian Savulescu, Sir Louis Matheson Distinguished Visiting Professor at Monash University, and Russell Powell, Assistant Professor of Philosophy at Boston University

The display of a frozen mammoth in Japan has again raised questions as to the possibility of creating a live born clone of extinct animals.

Theoretically, mammoths could be cloned by recovering, reconstructing or synthesising viable mammoth DNA and injecting it into the egg cell of a modern elephant whose nuclear DNA has been removed; alternatively, mammoth genetic material could be introduced into an elephant genome in order to create a mammoth-elephant hybrid or chimera.

This raises an ethical question as to whether we should start the journey down one of these paths.

Habitat disruption

Some people worry about the match between an extinct clone or novel chimera and the modern natural habitat. Firstly, there are worries that introducing these new species could disrupt natural ecosystems, or the so-called 'balance of nature'. This was one of the many ethical themes in the novel and film *Jurassic Park*. Perhaps extinct animals are dead for a good ecological reason, so to speak, and 'unnaturally' re-introducing them, particularly those that vanished long ago, would be futile or even pose serious global risks to life on the planet.

This is a common concern that should be addressed. Mammoths were widely around until 10,000 years ago, with some surviving until as recently as 4,000 years ago. Mammoths are thus not particularly 'alien' organisms from a modern ecological standpoint. They lived and evolved alongside much of the modern flora and fauna, including humans – who are, incidentally, likely responsible for their extinction. It is therefore highly unlikely that the introduction of a mammoth population would severely perturb natural ecosystems.

In any case, the extent to which there really is a 'benevolent balance of nature' has been vigorously contested in biology. Food webs are often maintained despite significant fluctuations in extinction, invasion, migration, diversity, and energy pathways.

Resurrecting an extinct animal

A second concern regards the well-being of the cloned animal itself. Mammoths are social creatures, and if one or more of them were produced and kept in an artificial environment, such as a zoo, or were subject to disturbing experimental conditions, it could be distressing and painful for them. This concern would be even greater if we were re-creating extinct species with even higher cognitive functions, such as Neanderthals or human-chimp chimeras – something that is also theoretically possible.

The critical ethical issue in re-creating extinct species, or in creating new kinds of animals, is to first determine through careful scientific study what is in their interests and to ensure that they live good lives in the world in which they are created. Creating favourable conditions for extinct animals or novel chimeras might require modifying or creating new habitats in which they can flourish.

This point is crucial. We cannot always know in advance whether the introduction of a new species will be good or bad for the animal introduced, or for other animals, including humans, communities and ecosystems. Once a new animal is created, it should not be introduced into the wild or into captivity until it is humanely studied to evaluate its own interests, and the threat it might pose to others.

However, if we are confident that a cognitively sophisticated

organism, such as a mammoth, would lead a good life, this may provide moral reasons to create it – whether or not that animal is a clone of a member of an extinct lineage.

But why bother?

Richard Dawkins recently tweeted,

Why bother (to clone mammoths)? Why bother? Why bother to go on living? Why not just stop breathing if you are that incurious?

– Richard Dawkins
(@RichardDawkins) 15 July 2013

But it is not just curiosity that drives the imperative to introduce extinct, novel or threatened species. We now have the power not only to obliterate life from the planet, but also to protect and manage it.

We should decide what kind of life there should be. We should invest in technologies that allow us to maintain biological diversity and perhaps even increase it. Some might even argue that humans have a particular moral obligation to re-introduce species whose extinction they caused, either directly, as is likely in the case of the mammoth, or indirectly, as a result of global climatic disruption.

The value of re-creating mammoths might consist largely in satisfying intrinsic human curiosity. But, creating or re-creating some kinds of life forms may also be of great instrumental value to human beings, say in blocking the emergence of pathogens, or in helping to ensure the continued existence of life on the planet. What initially seems like a curiosity actually prompts a deep question about the role of humans in directing the future course of life on this planet.

Up until this point, human influence on the world has largely been destructive. But we are now entering a phase where our influence can be constructive. We can now preserve species not merely by conservation of the environment, but also through the use of genetic engineering, synthetic biology, and other reproductive technologies.

Is biological intervention 'playing God'?

Many people believe that environmental interventions are preferable to and should be prioritised over biological ones, but we think and have argued that so urgent are our problems, we must explore all options, including using knowledge of the biological sciences to possibly deal with social or environmental problems. There are four ways to achieve any goal, be it human survival, species diversity, or global security: modify the environment, society, human psychology or biology. All options should be explored.

Some object to 'deep' human intervention in nature, like the cloning of extinct organisms or the creation of chimeric organisms, on the grounds that such interventions amount to 'playing God'. Since humans intervene in nature all the time and for good moral reasons, for example medicine, there cannot be something inherently morally problematic about such interventions. The focus should instead be on the types of harms that we identified above.

There has been much discussion about whether synthetic biology could really create artificial life. A much more profound and pressing ethical question asks what kinds of life forms there should be. It is now within our power to decide.

24 July 2013

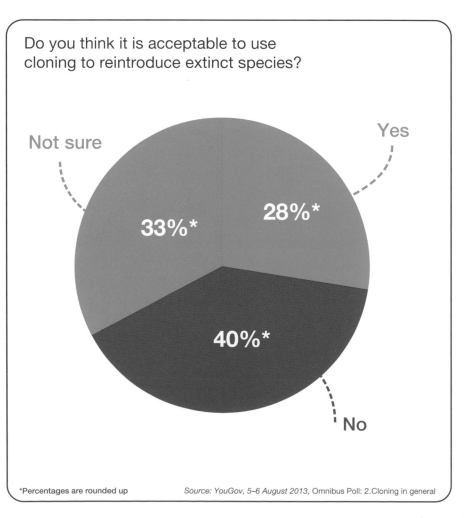

Do you think it is acceptable to use cloning to reintroduce extinct species?

Not sure 33%*

Yes 28%*

No 40%*

*Percentages are rounded up

Source: YouGov, 5–6 August 2013, Omnibus Poll: 2.Cloning in general

Mammoths are a huge part of my life. But cloning them is wrong

Instead of the romantic idea of bringing an ice age animal back to life, shouldn't we put our best efforts into saving endangered elephants?

By Tori Herridge

In 2013 a remarkably well-preserved mammoth was excavated from the permafrost on Maly Lyakhovsky island, northern Siberia. It was May, and a balmy -10°C. Snow lay on the ground. But when the team cut into the frozen carcass, a dark red-brown fluid oozed out. A fluid that looked exactly like blood.

Nothing like this had ever been seen before, and hopes ran high – still run high, in fact – that this might hold the key to mammoth cloning.

For a while, the likelihood of anyone getting anywhere at all with such a project was so remote it seemed pointless to worry – why talk about 'should', when there was no 'could'? But two groups with two different approaches – Sooam in South Korea and George Church's lab in the US – are committed to taking their cloning efforts from the theoretical to the actual, from the lab to the tundra. As these cloning efforts gather steam, it's time to have a serious conversation about the ethics of cloning.

I'm a paleobiologist at the Natural History Museum in London, and I live, sleep and dream mammoths. I doubt that there are many people in the world who would like to see a real-life woolly mammoth as much as I do. And yet I think cloning one would be ethically flawed.

Any attempt to clone a mammoth would probably require a living elephant – likely to be Asian – to act as a surrogate. To go through 22 months of pregnancy, carrying an animal of a completely different species as part of the experiment. An intelligent, social animal, at the brink of extinction, and one we know doesn't do all that well in captivity.

And not just one elephant. In reality, many surrogates would be needed before a successful baby mammoth was born.

There are very good reasons for using animals in scientific research, but there are also strict ethical codes of practice that demand that the potential benefits of the research outweigh the suffering to the animals involved.

Does the potential benefit to humanity of cloning a mammoth outweigh the suffering an Asian elephant surrogate mother might experience? I've yet to hear a convincing argument that it does.

So, why should we clone a mammoth? Because it would be cool to see one? That's not going to cut it, I'm afraid.

Because it advances technology and the sum total of human knowledge? OK – but why a mammoth? Why not some other extinct creature that could be born of a surrogate better suited to life in captivity, or one that

requires no animal surrogate at all? Church's group are also trying to bring back the passenger pigeon, for example, and here it's only the eggs that are manipulated in the lab. Granted, that's not possible for mammals, but maybe a mouse would be a better starting point. For some reason, however, cloning an obscure species of extinct rodent doesn't seem to capture the imagination.

What about the advances that could be made in understanding elephant reproductive biology? After all, zoo breeding programmes for elephants aren't hugely successful, and Asian elephants are on the brink of extinction. So why not just put the effort in to doing the research into the reproductive biology of those living species where the results may be more directly transferable? If the reason is that it's easier to get

HOW ARE YOU ON IRONY?

...IT'S MY MOTHER, SHE'S GONE EXTINCT HASN'T SHE...?

funding for cloning a mammoth, then all of us need to take a good long look at our priorities.

Because by bringing back the woolly mammoth, we could restore the ecosystem of the mammoth steppe and potentially stabilise the tundra terrain in the high Arctic? The idea being that this would mitigate the risk of permafrost melt, and the release of huge amounts of methane gas stored there, which would be bad news for our already warming planet. The problem here is that we don't yet fully understand the role of the woolly mammoth as an ecosystem engineer, and it is unclear still whether the mammoth steppe disappeared as a result of the loss of the mammoth or whether the mammoth disappeared because its habitat was lost, along with its ice age world. It's a big gamble to put your climate-change mitigation hopes on a herd of woolly mammoths – and if it did work, it would require numbers in the hundreds of thousands to have an effect. That's going to take a long time, and a lot of surrogate elephant mums, to achieve. And have you seen the rate at which climate change seems to be progressing?

It will make a huge amount of money for the person who clones – and maybe patents – the woolly mammoth. After all, for all my protests, I'd pay to see one if it was there, wouldn't you? This might justify the economic outlay, but an ethical justification it is not. I think that the real reason – the only reason really – that people want to clone a mammoth is the hope of salvation.

There's a reason the terms 'de-extinction' and 'rewilding' are so powerful and that's because they imply a return to a time, a state of grace, a place that was somehow unspoiled. Cloning a mammoth offers us the hope of undoing the excesses of humanity, bringing back the creatures whose extinction we helped bring about. I see it in people's eyes when I explain that Church's CRISPRs method isn't cloning exactly, more just making a genetically engineered elephant that can handle the cold – this just isn't as emotionally satisfying as the Sooam approach: taking an actual mammoth cell nucleus, DNA intact, and popping that into an elephant egg. People want to believe they are getting back the 'real thing'. I get it. Sometimes

the ice age world is so real to me that my throat aches and my eyes sting a little when I think about what we've lost, the animals we will never see. But here's the irony – if we feel like that about the mammoth, just think how our kids might feel about the elephant if we let it become extinct. We really ought to be focusing on that, and doing everything we can to stop it from happening.

Tori Herridge took part in the autopsy of the Maly Lyakhovsky Mammoth (aka Buttercup), which aired in Woolly Mammoth: the Autopsy, *on Channel 4 on 23 November at 8pm*

18 November 2014

DNA study says cloning dinosaurs is impossible

By Michael Rundle

While DNA cloning of dinosaurs seemed feasible in *Jurassic Park* – especially if you were ten years old when the movie came out – scientists now say it is impossible.

The study found that after cells die enzymes start to break down the bonds between nucleotides that form DNA.

After time, micro-organisms and reactions with water further degrade the material, until gradually there is little of the original DNA left.

After about 521 years only half of the DNA remains, according to the study in the *Proceedings of the Royal Society*.

Almost every bond of DNA would be destroyed after 6.8 million years, the study estimates.

It would cease to be readable after about 1.5 million years ago – long enough to perhaps do cool science with a woolly mammoth, but not dinosaurs, the last of which died 65 million years ago.

'This confirms the widely held suspicion that claims of DNA from dinosaurs and ancient insects trapped in amber are incorrect,' said Simon Ho, an evolutionary biologist at the University of Sydney in Australia.

The record for an authentic DNA sequence is currently 500,000 years, meaning scientists can theoretically go further back – but not anywhere close to a velociraptor.

Which, to anyone who's watched beyond the first hour of *Jurassic Park*, is surely a good thing?

11 October 2012

For me, the idea of de-extinction is now as dead as a dodo

An article from The Conversation.

THE CONVERSATION

By Robert John Young, Professor of Wildlife Conservation at University of Salford

My wildlife friends and I often talk about what species we would bring back from extinction. I am torn between the dodo and the thylacine, also known as the Tasmanian tiger. This was once a speculative, sci-fi debate but not anymore. Ever since Dolly the sheep was cloned, conservation biologists have mooted the idea and the process of de-extinction – bringing back dead species – is coming closer to reality.

De-extinction can be achieved by one of two means: selective breeding or cloning. In the selective breeding method we try to re-create extinct species such as the aurochs (extinct large cattle from Europe and Asia) by looking for their surviving genes among existing cattle and breeding animals to favour these genes. Then you compare the genome of the resulting animals with that for aurochs until you have what is genetically an auroch.

The second method essentially involves finding the DNA of an extinct species and inserting it into a recipient egg cell and recipient animal – the cloning process. This second process is limited to species that have gone extinct more recently (hundreds of years) because you need to find intact DNA, so I am afraid there will be no Jurassic Park. We would also need to find DNA from several different individuals otherwise we would end up with problems due to inbreeding, such as those seen in white tigers.

Unsurprisingly the 'instant fix' of cloning has received more interest as it would not depend on many generations of captive breeding. A wide range of species have been suggested for cloned de-extinction from the dodo to the woolly mammoth.

Initially, I liked the idea. I'd love to see a dodo in a zoo or even better to see wild woolly mammoths on an ecotourism trip to the steppes of Siberia. But such meddling raises a host of questions.

For instance, an African elephant would be the obvious recipient for woolly mammoth DNA. But as mammals learn a considerable part of their behaviour from their parents and peers – are we not just creating an elephant in mammoth's clothing? It would, therefore, seem our resurrected animals would need some kind of training to survive in the wild, which may not be unlike the survival training reintroduced zoo animals already receive.

If a species was successfully reintroduced and its population grew to previous levels it would have a major ecological impact. The animals which have occupied its ecological space may find themselves squeezed out. Governments would, rightly, be very cautious about the reintroduction of such animals.

Show me the money

Given the limited money available for wildlife conservation, it's not clear that the expense of bringing back the dodo makes sense. A simple utilitarianism would suggest not; the cost of resurrecting the dodo could be used to save many other living species from extinction. For example, it now appears that a cloning approach may be the only solution to save the northern white rhinoceros from extinction – there are now only five individuals left.

However society, thankfully, does not always run according to such utilitarian analyses. So perhaps the dodo will have its day – even if that is just living in a zoo. It may behave like a farmyard chicken but it would still be a powerful symbol for species conservation: I suspect some zoos would be shedding their giant pandas to go into dodos.

Dead as a dodo

But what kind of symbol would a living dodo be? It can no longer be the symbol of extinction; the Rubber Dodo Award for people who have contributed most to species extinction would need to be renamed. It would be testimony to how far science has come and how far science can take us.

But this sense of scientific wonder isn't always helpful. A living dodo would give out the wrong message to society and politicians – we can destroy anything we like and scientists will eventually find a way to fix it. This seems, for example, to be the hope with climate change.

As a species I think we need to accept responsibility for what we have done to this planet and not have blind faith that in the future scientists will fix all of our mistakes. We need to live with our mistakes and learn from them. It is for this reason I am not wishing for de-extinction.

18 December 2014

Key facts

⇨ The types of cloning differ widely from one another, both in their techniques and aims. (page 1)

⇨ Although the first cloned animal – a tadpole – was created in 1952, the most publicly significant event in the history of cloning was the creation of Dolly the sheep in 1996 at the Roslin Institute, near Edinburgh. (page 1)

⇨ In 2005 Professor Ian Wilmut, the creator of Dolly the Sheep, was granted a licence to clone human embryos for medical research – a decision which attracted considerable criticism. (page 2)

⇨ In 1903, U.S. Department of Agriculture employee Herbert Webber coins the word 'clon' (which evolves into 'clone') to refer to 'any group of cells or organisms produced asexually from a single sexually produced ancestor'. (page 4)

⇨ In 2001, Noah, a gaur and the first of an endangered species to be cloned, is produced by Advanced Cell Technologies. (page 5)

⇨ In 2005, Snuppy, the first clone of a dog, is produced at Seoul National University in South Korea. (page 5)

⇨ It takes about 30 years to breed a banana from seed, so, to speed the process of getting fruit to market, most bananas, potatoes, apples, grapes, pears and peaches are from clones. (page 10)

⇨ Clones are born just like any other animal. The only difference is that clones don't require a sperm and egg to come together to make an embryo. Clone embryos are made by using a whole cell or cell nucleus from a donor animal and fusing it to an egg cell that's had its nucleus removed. (page 10)

⇨ Cloning and the genetic manipulation of humans – eugenics – have become established narrative tropes in cinema. The main recurring themes are filiation, human 'uniqueness' and difference, instrumentality, and totalitarian or rigidly class-based societies. (page 12)

⇨ Some people may have a stem cell transplant using stem cells from umbilical cord blood. (page 15)

⇨ 80% of EU citizens supported embryonic stem cell research (up from 53% in 2005). (page 19)

⇨ 67% supported research with human embryonic stem cells (up from 41% in 2005). (page 19)

⇨ When it comes to scientific research on human, plant and animal DNA (out of all the people polled) 11% worry that this research poses unforeseen dangers, 38% are excited that this reach could lead to major scientific breakthroughs, 33% agree with both previous statements, 6% agree with neither and 12% are unsure. (page 19)

⇨ A survey carried out on over 1,700 UK adults aged 16+, conducted on behalf of the UK Government, identified that 57% of UK citizens feel the benefits of stem cell research outweigh any potential risks and 90% had heard of 'stem cells' but only 34% felt 'well-informed' about them. (page 20)

⇨ Globally there is a great disparity in awareness of stem cells – from 33% (Japan) to 86% (Sweden, Denmark) of respondents having heard of stem cells. (page 20)

⇨ Different religions view the status of the early human embryo in different ways. For example, the Roman Catholic, Orthodox and conservative Protestant Churches believe the embryo has the status of a human from conception and no embryo research should be permitted. Judaism and Islam emphasise the importance of helping others and argue that the embryo does not have full human status before 40 days, so both these religions permit some research on embryos. (page 22)

⇨ Test tube meat, being a possible answer to the cultivation of livestock, produces 78–96% less CO_2, according to the EU and research from the University of Oxford. (page 30)

⇨ Meat and milk from cloned animals are classed as 'novel foods' under the EU Novel Foods Regulation (1997). This means they must be assessed for safety before they can be legally marketed anywhere in the EU. (page 31)

⇨ Cloned horses are allowed in a range of competitions (they were allowed in the 2012 Olympics). (page 33)

⇨ The average cost to clone a horse is around $150,000. (page 33)

⇨ When asked if they think it is acceptable to use cloning to reintroduce extinct species, people who were polled replied: 28% Yes, 40% no and 33% were unsure. (page 36)

⇨ Scientists estimate that almost every bond of DNA would be destroyed after 6.8 million years. Therefore this study suggests that cloning dinosaurs is impossible. (page 38)

Clone

An organism which is genetically identical to another. Identical twins are an example of naturally occurring clones, although scientists are also able to create cloned organisms in a laboratory.

Cloning

The asexual reproduction of identical copies of an original. Cloning is an extremely controversial area of scientific research – human cloning, and to a lesser extent animal cloning, for reproductive purposes has caused considerable concern with the public.

DNA

DNA (deoxyribonucleic acid) is the genetic coding which is present in every cell of living organisms. DNA is found in the nucleus of each cell and determines the characteristics for that organism.

Dolly the sheep

Dolly was the first animal to be cloned from an adult mammal in 1996 at the Roslin Institute, near Edinburgh – representing a scientific breakthrough. Dolly became very well known amongst the public, but died prematurely due to a disease of the lungs.

Embryo

An animal in the earliest stages of development. In humans, this refers to the eight weeks following conception. After this point the developing baby is referred to as a foetus.

Food Standards Agency

An independent government department set up to protect the public's health and consumer interests in relation to food. The Food Standards Agency is responsible for monitoring the marketing of products from cloned animals and their offspring, in conjunction with the relevant EU legislation.

Genes

A gene is an instruction and each of our cells contains tens of thousands of these instructions. In humans, these instructions work together to determine everything from our eye colour to our risk of heart disease. The reason we all have slightly different characteristics is that before we are born our parents' genes get shuffled about at random. The same principles apply to other animals and plants.

Genetic modification

May also be called modern biotechnology, gene technology, recombinant DNA technology or genetic engineering. Scientists are able to modify genes in order to produce different characteristics in an organism than it would have produced naturally. GM techniques allow specific genes to be transferred from one organism to another, including between non-related species. This technology might be used, for example, to produce plants which are more resistant to pesticides, which have a higher nutritional value, or which produce a greater crop yield. Those in favour of GM say that this could bring real benefits to food producers and consumers. Those against GM feel it is risky as scientists do not have the knowledge to 'play God' with the food we eat.

In vitro fertilisation

A technique where the egg is fertilised by sperm outside of the body.

Reproductive cloning

The process of creating an organism from the cell of an existing organism, resulting in a genetically identical 'clone'. Scientists transfer the cell nucleus containing the DNA into an unfertilised egg and allow the egg to divide. The fertilised egg is then allowed to develop to full term (in a surrogate carrier's womb in the case of mammals).

Stem cells

There are two sources of stem cells: adult and embryonic. Whereas scientists think that adult stem cells are restricted to maintaining the health of the tissue where they are found, embryonic stem cells have the potential to turn into any cell type. If we can harness their adaptability, they might be a source of healthy tissue to replace that which is diseased or damaged in adults. However, because the embryo is destroyed during the process, the extraction and use of embryonic stem cells is highly controversial. Pro-life groups in particular have been campaigning against stem cell research, as they believe human life begins at conception and embryos should be afforded the same rights as adult humans.

Therapeutic cloning

Also known as somatic cell nuclear transfer to avoid confusion with reproductive cloning, which is a completely different process. Therapeutic cloning involves the creation of embryonic stem cell 'lines' by injecting the nucleus of a somatic cell into an unfertilised egg. Scientists are then able to create many embryonic stem cells, all of which are genetically identical to the DNA from the original nucleus.

Assignments

Brainstorming

⇨ In small groups, discuss what you know about cloning. Consider the following questions:

- What is a clone?

- Why are scientists interested in cloning?

- Why is cloning controversial?

- What is a stem cell?

Research

⇨ Carry out a survey to find out whether the pupils in your class would eat meat from a cloned cow. Write an analysis of your findings, including graphs to display your results.

⇨ The laws which regulate cloning are constantly being reviewed and updated. Visit the Food Standards Agency's website to find out about current legislation and advice. Do you think the Food Standards Agency are successfully regulating animal cloning for food?

⇨ In pairs, create a PowerPoint presentation that explains what stem cell research is and what it is used for. Try to condense the information into six to eight accessible slides.

⇨ Look at *A timeline of the evolution of animal breeding* on page 4. Has there been any more significant advancements in cloning? Continue this timeline with updated events and present it in a creative way.

Design

⇨ Pretend you work for The Anthony Nolan charity (www.anthonynolan.org). They have a register to match people willing to donate their bone marrow or blood stem cells to people who need transplants. Create a leaflet with helpful information about stem cell transplants and what kind of support The Anthony Nolan charity offers for patients and families going through a transplant (e.g. they provide information, support and an online forum).

⇨ Imagine you work for a company that sells food from cloned animals (e.g. meat or milk). Create a poster advertising your chosen food product and think up ways you can encourage and persuade people to try it.

⇨ Choose an illustration from this book and write a paragraph exploring what the artist was trying to portray with his image.

Oral

⇨ Split into two groups and have the following debate: one group supporting the idea of developing human cloning research, whilst the other should present arguments against human cloning.

⇨ In groups, roleplay a radio interview on the topic of animal cloning for food. One member of the group should play the role of the host, one a scientist keen to pursue animal cloning as a method of food production, one a representative of a faith group who opposes cloning, one a member of a lobby group which addresses the world hunger crisis, one a representative of an animal welfare group against the idea of animal cloning and one a member of the public who is yet to be swayed either way. Debate the topic for around 15 minutes.

⇨ Discuss in groups the following question: do you think cloned racehorses should be allowed? Why or why not? You might find reading *Cloning in racehorses* useful (page 33).

⇨ Read *Animal rights groups slam cloning of British dog, Winnie the dachshund* on page 34. In pairs, discuss why people would want to clone their pet and also consider who might be against the cloning pets – why is this?

Reading/writing

⇨ Write an article for a magazine which explains the differences between therapeutic cloning and reproductive cloning in an easy to understand way. Members of the public often assume that the term 'cloning' refers solely to the genetic replication of organisms. Your article should dispel the myths surrounding the topic of cloning and inform readers of the processes involved with therapeutic cloning and its uses, compared with reproductive cloning.

⇨ There are many science fiction films which deal with the subject of cloning: for example, *The 6th Day*, *The Island*, *Blade Runner* and *Moon*. Why do you think this is such a popular theme? Watch one of these films and write a review which considers how the theme of cloning is explored throughout the film.

⇨ Read the book, or watch the film, *Never Let Me Go* by Kazuo Ishiguro. Write a book review that analyses the author (or director's) portrayal of the theme of cloning.

⇨ Should cloning be used to resurrect extinct animals? Why or why not? Write a blog post which considers the positives and negatives not only for the extinct species but for wider society and the environment/food chain as well.

Acknowledgements

The publisher is grateful for permission to reproduce the material in this book. While every care has been taken to trace and acknowledge copyright, the publisher tenders its apology for any accidental infringement or where copyright has proved untraceable. The publisher would be pleased to come to a suitable arrangement in any such case with the rightful owner.

Images

All images courtesy of iStock, except page 14 © Tareq Salahuddin, page 23 © Seatano Lacerda, page 28 © Morguefile and page 33 © SXC.

Icons on pages 9, 13 and 31 are reproduced courtesy of Freepik.

Illustrations

Don Hatcher: pages 17 & 25. Simon Kneebone: pages 1 & 37. Angelo Madrid: pages 12 & 34.

Additional acknowledgements

Editorial on behalf of Independence Educational Publishers by Cara Acred.

With thanks to the Independence team: Mary Chapman, Sandra Dennis, Christina Hughes, Jackie Staines and Jan Sunderland.

Cara Acred

Cambridge

May 2015